PHANTOM LOBSTER

The Walmsley Society
www.walmsleysoc.org

Leo Walmsley

Phantom Lobster

A True Story

BY
Leo Walmsley

Foreword by Stephanie Walmsley

The Walmsley Society

First published in 1933 by Jonathan Cape Ltd.

This edition published in 2009 by
The Walmsley Society
www.walmsleysoc.org

ISBN   978-0-9534449-3-9

British Library Cataloguing-in-Publication Data:
A catalogue record is available for this book
from the British Library.

Printed and bound by

SRP
Exeter

Foreword

This is the story of a man in pursuit of a phantom, a dream; of how he schemes and plans, hoping to make his dream come true.

It is set in the village of Robin Hood's Bay on the east coast of Yorkshire, a village of great charm, of winding alleys, cobbled streets and red pantile roof cottages.

Living in semi-poverty, the author temporarily abandons work on his novel. Against a background of the roaring sea, with all its changing moods, its swells, the sudden calm, the thunderous crashing waves, a wonderful idea comes to him. It begins to germinate in his mind. He knows that the lives of his fisher friends, the Lunns, are controlled by the sea. He knows how they struggle . . . His mind is now filled with an exciting plan. He starts to work feverishly, sometimes all through the night, forgetting to eat, forgetting to light the fire in his chilly romantic cottage by the cliff edge.

He is going to measure his wits against the strength of the sea.

'Three whole weeks and only one day's fishing and

now it coming on bad again.'

A fisherman's life is not an easy one.

But things could change . . . perhaps . . . The author thinks they can. For this is also the story of a man's admiration and affection for his fishermen friends. It is them he wants to help, and all inshore fishers round the coast who share a desperate struggle to survive. His friends are fighters. They are brave, audacious in their contest with the sea.

The more he thinks of his plan, the more wonderful it seems. He is convinced it could revitalise the fishing industry and save what he describes as 'this magnificent breed of men from extinction'.

Yes, with his new invention he would revive a dying industry. It was a challenge, a thrilling one.

With high hopes he sets out on a journey to different parts of England, seeking help and expert advice for his scheme. His travels take him to London where he tramps round, cold and hungry, in freezing fog-bound weather. He meets a variety of influential people, financiers, millionaires. He goes to the House of Commons and is given an excellent lunch.

But the author's heart is never far from Robin Hood's Bay, his childhood home. He often yearns for the sound of the breakers, the gales rattling his bedroom windows, the cries of the gulls as they swoop down over the beautiful curve of the bay, High Batts and Low Batts cliff. He wants to feel again the spray on his face when fishing with the Lunns in their wildly pitching coble.

He misses Marney Lunn opening his cottage door at 5am, shouting up the stairs:

'Come on! Look lively. We're going to launch the coble ... tide's just right.'

And he misses the generosity and kindness of these friends; the warmth and hospitality to be found in their bright cottage next to his:

'You're coming to supper aren't you? Amy's laid a place for you. She's baked a cheese-cake and a whole batch of tarts — they're champion! Come on.'

Reading *Phantom Lobster* makes you share the author's dreams and you hope so much that his ingenious, inventive mind will be rewarded, his friends given the chance to make a decent living again and that 'hundreds of pounds' will be put into their pockets.

And I think you will also hope that their staunch and loyal friend becomes solvent too.

Stephanie Walmsley

For
Jerry and Ann

AUTHOR'S NOTE

THIS book is the record of an actual experience. 'Bramblewick', as Marney Lunn would say, is a 'real spot'; and Marney himself, and the Fosdycks, are 'real folks'. I had, however, used the same 'spot' and the same 'folks' in my novel *Three Fevers,* and the names I had invented for them had stuck so hard in my mind that it was hard in this book — which is not a novel — to change them back. Bramblewick therefore stays Bramblewick, and Marney stays Marney: and to be consistent I have invented names for the new 'folks' who appear. There is no secret about Bramblewick. Its latitude and longitude are roughly, 54. 28.40. North. 0. 34. 10. West.

L.W.

BOOK ONE

1

'IF I'd had an education like yours,' said Marney Lunn, 'and I knew how to do so many sorts of things, I'm damned if I'd be living by myself in a spot like Bramblewick, in winter time; getting my own meals, and lugging firewood off the beach, and messing on with fisherfolks like us. I'm damned if I would. I'd find out what job I could do best, whether it was the job I liked best or not. I'd set to and make some brass. I'd save, and when I'd got enough, and got it properly invested, I'd travel all over the world. I'd go to spots like Miami and Naples and Honolulu; spots where I've been, only when I was there I had to stay on board ship and work harder than when I was at sea. I'd buy curios and things like that, and bring them back when I came back; and I'd have a nice little house Up-Bank, with every modern improvement in it for making you cosy, and a garden...'

'You've got back home quick enough,' his wife interrupted, drily. 'I wonder you'd bother to go.'

'That's only because I couldn't bear leaving you and the bairn so long.'

'Aye. I notice you're not taking us with you. Maybe

the others you left out foreign would object. . . .'

'There's still one word wanted. It's got five letters and it's got to begin with L. "Found in tropical forests." It will be a queer sort of animal with a foreign name. They always give you at least one word that no one's ever heard of.'

I chanced more coals on my head and suggested LIANA. Marney, to my relief however, re-applied himself to the cross-word puzzle. There was a minute's quiet, in which I heard the north-east wind rattle the sea-ward window of Marney Lunn's little kitchen parlour (which was always so bright and cosy on a winter's night), and the muffled roar of surf from Bramblewick Bay. Then Marney said,

'God! That's got it! Now fancy guessing a word like that bang off. What is it, a sort of monkey?'

I felt that I had said enough, and did not answer; and Marney was too excited to pursue his quest for irrelevant information.

'Well, it's right, anyway,' he said. 'Look, it fits down and across. And that finishes the thing too. It can't help but be right, unless there's some trick in it. We're sure of a share in that five hundred quid, even if there's a thousand to share it. Last week there was only about a hundred. They got nearly five quid each. I'll slip down and get a postal order and get it off. I think we stand a damned good chance this time. I'd have never thought of a word like that, or those others you gave us, if I'd gone on trying for ever. You fill it in, Amy, your writing's clearer than mine.'

Marney moved his chair round to the fire, which

glowed fiercely with the frosty wind. He lit a fag.

'You know I'm serious about what I was just saying,' he went on expansively. 'It's none of my business, I know, but I believe in speaking what's in my mind. It just beats me why a chap of your education and ability should be wasting his time in a spot like this. In these days education counts above everything. It's my belief there's nothing you couldn't do if you gave your mind to it. Look at the way you took that magneto of ours to bits the other day, and put it right, and how you mended that compass card. You can take photos, and draw likenesses of folks. You know more about fish and things that live in the sea than any chap I ever met. You know all about fossils, and history and flint implements, and how the human body works inside. Damned if I knew properly how a kid was born until you told me. Then look at that lettering you did on our coble the other day. It's champion. I say it's a pity if you've got a natural gift for something, and you don't make the best use of it. You ought to remember that bit in the Bible about the chaps who had certain talents. There was one. . .'

'For God's sake, dry up.' Amy interrupted again, 'you're worse than a local preacher when you get started. *You* needn't talk about folks wasting their talents. If you'd stuck to sea and studied hard, you'd have had your master's ticket by now; and we might be living in that house of yours, Up-Bank, with a drawing-room maybe, and a tiled bathroom. Aye, and a nurse in a starched collar and cuffs to wash the bairn, while I take a little run in the motor car for the sake of my health. The only talent you've had that you haven't wasted is your talent for

3

telling other folks how to do their own jobs.'

Marney was rattled. He could only retort, feebly:

'Don't talk so daft. And anyway that's got nowt to do with what I was just saying. I was talking about him, not me.'

'Well, it's rude to talk like that about anybody until you're asked. Go down and get that postal order before it's too late. If there's a chance of us winning five hundred pounds it will be a pity to throw it away through missing the post. We could do with that money, and no mistake. Three whole weeks, and only one day's fishing in the lot, and now it coming on bad again. I'm sick to death of the sound of those breakers. . . . You can hurry straight back too,' she added. 'There's that fish to fillet for supper.'

I felt no resentment against Marney for his goodnatured homily, or its implications; but I had no wish to tell him what good reason, apart from financial exigency, had brought me back to my native place to live the life which he thought so wasteful: to tell him that I was concerned with the creation of a noble work of art, and that this apparent indolence of mine was simply a great preparation, a lying fallow. I was grateful to Amy; and I was glad that Marney, as we walked down to the post office together, did not pursue that subject which she had so skilfully turned aside. The fact that he carried in his hand a piece of paper with a potential value of five hundred pounds, had seized his imagination.

'God,' he muttered. 'It would be a bit of rare luck if we were the *only* ones to get it right. There's no reason why we shouldn't be. Dozens of these crossword puzzle competitions have been won by just one person. You see pictures of them in the paper, "Being Handed the Cheque" and the chap who's getting it smiling; and it's usually some poor devil who needs it badly, unemployed, or disabled by sickness. And the prize has got to be won. The paper itself guarantees that. I bet that last word you gave us would stump nine folks out of ten. Fancy getting five hundred quid just for writing down a few words, and the only expense a sixpenny postal order. You'd wonder how it could pay them to do it. It's money for nowt.'

I waited for Marney outside the post office; then, at his suggestion, we walked down to the Dock and the breakwater, to have a look at the weather. We were nearing the end of one of the worst Octobers the fisher-men of Bramblewick had ever known. It was not that there had been a record number of gales, or any gales of record severity; but that strong winds had blown with an extraordinary monotony from between south-east and north-east, maintaining a swell which, if not dangerous even to fishing craft clear of the land, effectively blocked the entrance to Bramblewick's landing, and kept the two local craft ashore. There had been a respite yesterday. Both boats had gone off, and had done fairly well. This morning too, there had been a windless dawn, with only a moderate sea, and the boats had been launched. But the sun had scarcely cleared the horizon when a strong wind had blown up from the north-east, quickly raising the swell again; and fishing had been abandoned.

We halted in the lee of the breakwater wall, out of the rush of cold wind from the sea. The moon, approaching full, had risen over High Batts, and from the village to the

5

foot of that distant headland the surf broke in long, curving lines of dazzling whiteness upon the buried scaurs which in places reached out half a mile from the shore. The noise was deep and continuous. Marney was not cheerful now.

'It's a devil,' he muttered. 'It's enough to give anyone the pip. If only it would blow a real gale and be done with it. It's this half-hearted sort of weather that gets on my nerves. There's less wind now than there was at dinner-time. It will very likely fall to nothing before morning. But the swell will take another day to fall away, and by that time there'll be another breeze ready round the corner. I tell you I'm just about fed up with Bramblewick. If I could raise enough brass I'd persuade our old man and John to buy a bigger boat and go to Burnharbour. You can put to sea there almost any weather. We could be fishing now if it wasn't for that blasted landing. I hate staying ashore. I hate having nowt to do.'

I wondered if Marney's unusual depression was due to the weather, or if there was not a more subtle explanation of it in the way he turned round and looked across the Dock, that open space hemmed in by cottages where the boats are kept in bad weather.

'Do you know,' he muttered, 'I sometimes feel I'd like to bury a load of dynamite under all this, and blow the whole damned spot to bits. I don't know why, but I just hate Bramblewick sometimes. It gets on my nerves.'

We parted at the foot of Chapel Street, after I had refused a pressing invitation to go back and have supper and 'stay on'. I carried on up the Dock, which becomes the 'Road' where the cottages narrow on it, and follows the covered-in course of Bramblewick Beck to the back end of the village. It was dark here, for the street lamps are not lit on moonlight nights, and the moon was still low. The tall walls of the cottages gave shelter from the wind, but between them the noise of the sea was stronger than in the Dock, making a great rushing sound like a spating stream in a narrow gorge. The Road was deserted. The bakery on my right hand was already closed. Farther up on the left, a light in the fried fish shop escaped through a thin cloud of smelly steam. Nearer, on my right, a single gas lamp in the back of Willy Coulson's shop indicated that he was about to close. I hurried in for a packet of Vim and a tin of gold flake to 'go down' on my account.

I went back towards the Dock, and turned up a dark winding alley, that climbed steeply past rows of closely packed cottages until I came to one that led to the landward margin of the village. I had a glimpse of the moon again, with a strip of ragged cloud flying past it; I felt the wind, and the sound of the sea became harsher. My cottage was the last but one of the row on my right.

I had no sooner stepped inside of it, however, and shut the door, and struck a match to light the gas, than there were shuffling footsteps on the cobbles outside, and an urgent knock. I opened the door to find Mrs. Brewster my next-door neighbour. There was anxiety in her manner and voice.

'Eh—I hope I'm not troubling you,' she said, 'but please can you tell me what they call a thing that ships used during war time to cut away mines? It's for a cross-word puzzle. It's got eight letters, and the second two are A R, and the next but one is V.'

I suggested instantly the word PARAVANE.

'Eh!' she ejaculated. 'Would you mind saying it again please. Or would you mind writing it down. I've got a pencil and a bit of paper.'

She handed them to me. She was a fat, agreeable little person, hardened but not conquered by a life of much misfortune. She was not like her husband Reub, pure 'Bramblewick'. He was a boat-builder by trade, a first-rate craftsman who couldn't bear not finishing a job 'off proper'. He liked to have all screws neatly counter-sunk, points filed off, joints fitting so close you couldn't put a sheet of paper between them; all wood sand-papered and smoothed. But there was no boat-building left in Bramblewick, and he did odd joinery, and fished for salmon in the summer in a small boat he had built for himself. He was small, harassed looking, with a long untidy moustache which accentuated the thinness of his face; but he was wiry, courageous and fertile, and he had fathered a large healthy family, the whole of which had to be accommodated in the tiny cottage next door.

Mrs. Brewster thanked me. I could take no credit for the missing word, for it was one that Marney had promptly guessed. But I called after her as she hurried indoors,

'Did you get that one beginning with L? Found in tropical forests?'

'Oh yes, thank you. I got that all right. It was the first I found out. I've got them all now, thank you very much.

I'm in a hurry to get the post with it. To-morrow's the last day for getting it in for a prize.'

2

Lighting the gas, I was at once seized with a violent sense of revulsion. The cottage was what is known in Bramblewick as a summer letting place, and I was renting it through the agency of my grocer at 10s. a week, with the special proviso that this should go down on my account, and be settled later. But it was larger than the usual Bramblewick cottage, possessing a living room, two bedrooms, an attic, and a combination kitchen washhouse, on the opposite side of the street. The lady who owned it (a 'foreigner' to Bramblewick) was a lady of pretensions. She had spent a large sum having the living room modernized. The old kitchen range had been replaced by a slow combustion grate, with a tiled hearth and an imitation marble mantelpiece. The original cottage windows had been given a sash with plate glass, the walls had been covered with 'art' wall-paper, and the doors and other woodwork had been grained to represent pitchpine, and then brightly varnished.

The place had been furnished on a very fulsome scale. When I had viewed it first, the living room contained a large dining-table in the Jacobean manner of light varnished oak; a Chesterfield suite of two large easy chairs and a monstrous settee upholstered in speckled violet plush. There were six upholstered dining chairs to match, a convertible bed-easy chair, with bright emerald corduroy cushions; and the room had contained also, a large pedal sewing machine (which, with the machine folded made a table), a large carved Swiss clock, a mahogany sideboard, many vases, eight monochrome reproductions of Conversation Pieces in fumed oak frames, a large oval mirror, and in the fireplace, inside a brass fender, a set of brass tongs, poker, shovel, and brass dogs.

But the room also had one vast, empty cupboard. Into it had gone the easy chairs, the sideboard, all the dining chairs, the clock, the mirror, the pictures, the fireside set and the vases. The settee had defeated me. So too, had the sewing machine. Yet on these, and on the room in general, I had, in the phrase of modern domestic decoration, 'projected my own personality'; and it was this, perhaps more than the room itself, that produced such a quick sense of revulsion. Upon the settee was a pair of rubber thigh boots, an oilskin coat, a wool sweater, and several stockings. On the sewing machine was a loaf of bread (still in its wrapping), a bag of groceries, and now the carton of Vim, and the tin of fags. In the nearest corner was a fishing rod, a landing net, a gaff, and on the floor close by, a tin containing sea-water, and some live bait. On the easy chair of the suite, was a typewriter, a towel, and another pair of stockings. An open attaché case was on the table. It contained correspondence and sheets of manuscript which flowed over on to the table, cascaded on to the arms and cushions of the bed-chair (drawn close to the fireplace) and on to the floor, mingling with the disjointed pages of a newspaper, still another pair of stockings, a pair of shoes, and some ashes which like a stream of lava, had oozed over the brass fender from the congested grate. The fire was out.

The sheets of manuscript were each editions of the first page of a short story I had started to write some weeks ago. Some were almost full; others bore only the title of the story. The most complete, and latest edition lay on the table near the chair, just as I had left it when, some hours ago, I had decided to go out and look at the weather. Possibly, I thought, if I had not gone out, that page might have been positively completed; but it came to me suddenly as I glanced round the room, that a likely reason for my slow progress with that story which when finished and sold, might pay my rent, was the appalling muddle of my work-room.

A new-born resolution took the place of my despair. I decided that I would make an immediate and thorough clearance; first light my fire, boil some water, sweep the floor, put away everything that could be put away; wash up some dishes that were in the scullery; sort out the unwanted pages of my potboiler, and then in an atmosphere of relative cleanliness and harmony settle down to a good night's work.

I took off my coat, rolled up my sleeves, and started on the fireplace. The grate was of that type which slips out bodily. You turn it over, give it a tap, and it is clear of ashes; you put it back, stoke it with paper and sticks, and coal, put a light to it, and the fire, surprised and delighted by the amount of air, kindles easily. The ashes unfortunately remain, and in Bramblewick you are your own dustman. My hearth already contained the accumulations of several such tippings of the grate. The reason became obvious when, having lit the fire, and put the kettle on, I opened a cupboard and found two buckets already full of ashes. I remembered the moon, however. The midden was only a short walk across the village green.

The way to the green lay to my right, past the Brewster's cottage. As I stepped out I saw Mrs. Brewster with a shawl over her head, and a letter in her hand, hurrying down to the post office. There was a gap in the curtain of the cottage living room. I had a swift picture of Reub, affectionately bouncing the latest baby up and down on his knee, and of two small girls washing-up on a table which bore a mutilated Sunday newspaper, and what was evidently a crossword puzzle dictionary.

I turned sharply to my right again, round the end of the cottage, and reached the green. The moon was riding clear now. The stars shone brilliantly. The green was merely a narrow, roughish piece of land which at some remote period of Bramblewick's history, had slipped down from the hill above (on whose top was the new coastguard station). When the tide was up it was the village playground. A deep, irregular track, cut into the turf from east to west, made the traditional cricket pitch. You had a stone, or a fish-box, or an old lobster pot for a wicket. The shape of the ground was such that you could only bowl from the village end; but if the ball was kept low, the deeply-grooved track ensured that it would hit the wicket, unless stopped by the batsman.

In winter we played a game called 'shinney-ower'. It was a primitive hockey, played with sticks made of the thick, flexible stems of oar-weed (their roots cut so that they left a knob like a boy's fist); and there was a rule that if an opponent put himself on the wrong side of the ball, you were entitled to hit him as hard as you liked across his shins. There was a rule that he must not hit back; but this rule was rarely kept, and fights were more frequent than goals.

Fights! It came to me, as I walked along that historic track, carrying a bucket of ashes in each hand, that my most enduring memories of Bramblewick's village green were painful ones. Not that I had any real dislike for fighting. But if you were not pure 'Bramblewick', you were regarded as a foreigner and an outlaw, and anybody's game. In every fight the odds were so adjusted that I should be beaten. Either I had to fight a bigger boy, or take on two small ones; and on the rare occasions when I achieved some sort of victory, my triumph was short lived, for it was looked upon as a challenge to the honour of the village, and there was always some stout patriot to step in and finish me off. And I laboured under a still greater handicap, for my mother, while admitting the principle that self-defence was justified, put me under a solemn obligation that I must never be the first 'to strike the blow'. The first blow therefore could be delivered with judgement and confidence, usually to my nose, producing a violent sneezing fit which disabled me for a start. . .

As I approached the midden, a cat I knew advanced

ingratiatingly towards me; then, quickly discovering in a cat's way that the buckets contained no organic matter, sheered off on a fresh reconnaissance. The moonlight was exhilarating. It would be some time yet, I thought, before my kettle boiled. Having emptied the buckets, I set them down, and climbed a rough path to the ridge of the hill above. I was assailed at once by the full force of the north-east wind, and the roar of the sea. I had an uninterrupted view of Bramblewick and the bay beyond.

A railway poster artist, commissioned to produce a picture which would attract summer visitors to Bramblewick, would not have chosen this as his point of view. He would have drawn that well-known aspect of 'Bramblewick from the North Cliff', showing the bold headland of High Batts in the distance, a range of heather-clad hills — ideal for picnics — to the west, and a curve of sandy beach — so safe for bathers — sweeping down to a foreground of picturesque red-tiled cottages, the village itself. He would have used cobalt and veridian for the sea, and shown it smooth.

My present view, by day or by moonlight, defied the conventions of artistic composition. The foreground was split by the bare ridge of the hill on which I stood, as far down as the middle distance. Here, below eye level, the cottages began; but they made a chaotic mass north and south, without any satisfying connecting element with the continuing cliffs which shaped the Bay, or with the sea.

If you wished for a comprehensive survey, however, and not merely for the conformable and the picturesque, this view-point was good. It gave the entire range of the moorland hills, which, from the abrupt end of High Batts, swell inland and back again to the sea at Low Batts point, forming the great amphitheatre of Fylingdales. It gave most of the three miles of beach between High Batts and the village; the protecting scaurs which formed the fishermen's landing; and, foreshortened, the continuation of the beach to Low Batts. By day, you could look over your shoulder and see the village of Thorpe, a mile inland, the roads winding up to the moor and the hamlet of Rowe. Across the rear end of the deep ravine on whose sides old Bramblewick was built, you could see the steep road called Bramblewick Bank, climbing to the rows of semi-detached brick villas which, with the Victoria   Hotel, the new parish church and the railway station, bore the collective title of Up-Bank, a name pronounced with mocking reverence by the inhabitants of the old village; for to live Up-Bank was a mark of social distinction. Approaching it from Up-Bank, old Bramblewick was completely hidden until you reached the Bank top. From where I stood, the front, or the back, or the roof, or a chimney of almost every one of its four hundred odd cottages (packed into an area of not more than a quarter of a square mile) was visible. And for me the prospect had four dimensions. Here, between the physical confines of the seaward horizon, and the curving hills from north to west and south, and a time dimension of my life up to the war, were the makings of the book, which when the time was ripe, I intended to write.

It was not to be, even in fictional disguise, about myself. I had advanced thus far towards the conception

15

of this book. Its characters were to be drawn from the people of the place, not necessarily the true village folk, but from those who made up its unique assembly in the dimension of my pre-war experience. The original inhabitants of Bramblewick, the builders of the village, were fisherfolk of distant Scandinavian stock. There was a sixteenth century record of a Bramblewick 'fiscar towne, with a Dock, or bosome, a mile in length, and twenty bootes'. When the great north-east coast whale-fishing industry developed, however, there was a leakage of Bramblewick fishermen into the whaling fleets, voyaging into the Arctic Circle, a leakage that was maintained when whaling gave way to the purely commercial shipping industry of the eighteenth and nineteenth centuries. Bramblewick men made good seamen. They made good officers. They were sober, diligent, courageous, close-lipped, and close-fisted. They saved. They bought shares in the brigs, and barques and schooners in which they sailed: they became joint-owners. In a business sense they were good owners. They made 'brass'. They reinvested their brass in new ships. When steam came they were among the first to see that 'sail' was dead, and their 'brass' went into 'steam'. The 'brass' stayed in the family, too. Almost invariably a boy leaving school went straight to sea. As he got his mates' tickets, berths were waiting him. When he got his master's ticket he would not have to wait long for a ship. All his savings went into the company. And the outward sign of his success was the 'flitting' out of old Bramblewick into one of the new villas Up-Bank, to which he would retire only when old age compelled him to do so.

True that not all Bramblewick men became sailors or fishermen. There were boys born with a fierce hatred of the sea. They might, because their fathers made them, serve their time; but on reaching an age of defiance they would stay at home and become tradesmen, even farmers. Yet probably their sons would have just as strong a hatred of a life ashore, and prove equally defiant in obeying the call of the sea. It was true that not all of Bramblewick's seamen were materially successful. A man might be drowned, or killed on board ship, or die of fever 'out foreign' before he had saved enough to 'flit' Up-Bank. His widow and family would have to stay Down-Bank. A few drank too hard, and while they commanded ships, they never achieved the social elevation of a villa, even for the years of their retirement. Some could not obtain even a second mate's ticket, and served all their lives before the mast. They too, stayed Down-Bank.

In my earliest memories of Bramblewick, only one family of whole-time fishers, the Fosdycks, remained of the original stock: and of this family the father, Tom, had retired at the age of seventy-nine, leaving four middle-aged sons, but no grandson, to carry-on to another generation. There was a living in fishing, but no one had ever built a villa Up-Bank with it. Only two cobles were regularly employed at the time of that historic invasion of Sledburgh 'foreigners', which brought six cobles, and four virile families of fishers to the place.

The book which I intended to write lacked form at

present, as my visual aspect lacked form. Yet it seemed that in the peculiar attitude of Bramblewick to strangers, was a vague growing point for its design. This attitude, an active and remorseless hostility of Bramblewick children towards the children of strangers, was more subtle in the adult: so subtle that it became impersonal almost, a spirit of the place rather than of its people, whom a casual stranger would have found good-mannered and hospitable enough. The Sledburgh 'foreigners' (Sledburgh was only twenty miles south down the coast) had found no difficulty in obtaining cottages for themselves, and they were not charged more than the customary rents. When their families arrived, by train, there were neighbours to bring them cups of tea, mugs of hot milk 'for the bairns', and give them a hand with the 'things'. The Fosdycks had helped the men haul their cobles to the Dock, and carry up their gear. But these 'foreigners' must have been aware even then of that strong subtle spirit in the air which, in less than fifteen years, was to drive all but one family (the Lunns), back to the village they had come from.

My own parents had arrived in Bramblewick very much as the Sledburgh 'foreigners' had done: only that it was in the depth of winter, and they came in one friendless family, not in four. Some light-hearted student friend of my father, who had been on a sketching holiday in Bramblewick during the summer, had raved to him about the beauty of the place, the colour of the sea, the moors, the quaintness of the old town with its crooked streets and red-tiled roofs. Cottages could be obtained at ridiculous rents. Nothing could be simpler than to convert one into a studio. If you were not above pot-boiling, you could earn enough to keep you by selling sketches to the summer visitors. An ideal spot for a young artist with ambitions, a family, but no capital. And the villagers were kindness itself.

My parents had been touched by this kindness of the Bramblewick folk. It must have gone far to soften my mother's shock on entering that cottage in which she was destined to spend the next twenty years of her life, to find a fire burning in the living room, and a Yorkshire tea laid on a box by the fireside. The shock, however, to which in succession was added the shock of discovering the cottage had no drains; no water; that the fire 'smoked'; that the oven door was so warped it would not close; that the roof leaked, that the walls were incurably damp, had not affected her so much as the sense she had that the whole village was pervaded by a spirit of enduring enmity. . . .

A pack of dark storm clouds had gathered on the seaward horizon beyond Low Batts Point. A drift of cloud torn from the bank by the north-east wind flew overhead, and its moon shadow raced across the fields of Low Batts top towards the village. The tide was ebbing quickly. The baring scaur ends showed up in startling relief against the moon-lit lines of surf. I could distinguish among the cottages at the edge of the cliff, whose farther side falls sheer into the sea, the two attic windows of my old home, which adjoined the cottage now occupied by young Marney Lunn. Originally it had been a fisherman's cottage, but its previous tenant had carried on a small confectioner's business, and its ground floor room had been fitted with a shop window, shelves, and a counter. The floor joists however, had been gnawed through by rats, and one of dad's first jobs had been to mend the floor with a packing case which had contained the bare canvases, which, when painted, were to bring him fame, possibly fortune. Dad had no sense of enmity in the air! Between him and all miasmas (and most realities) was the impenetrable blanket of his own illusions. While mother with the instincts of a jungle animal imposed upon herself the immense task of saving at least her family of three sons from Bramblewick, dad transformed the shop into what he called a 'show-room', converted the ruins of another cottage into a studio; painted water-colour sketches of Bramblewick, 'South View', 'North View', 'From the Beach', 'Showing the Old Coastguard Station' (and such aspects as were likely to appeal to the visitors); made studies for his Academy pictures, which were to be in oils; dabbled in photography; and continued his practical experiments towards the perfection of his patent dish-washing machine, a machine for washing paint brushes, and a collapsible artist's easel.

My parents at least belonged to this book. Through them, I thought this theme of a spirit of enmity embodied in a village might be worked out with great dramatic effectiveness. Handicapped by a terrifying pride, which verged on snobbery, by a powerful strain of puritanism, by an Irish imagination, tempered only a little by the solid Lancashire strain that was in her, my mother schemed and slaved with one purpose, that her family should be put outside a sphere which, her instincts told her, was dangerous. She knew that the spirit of Bramblewick could be propitiated. She recognized, at least instinctively, that it came from an intense pride of a people, in themselves, and in their place. There was less enmity if you talked 'Bramblewick', and thought 'Bramblewick', and did what Bramblewick did! Bramblewick 'kids' in those days wore guernseys and corduroy trousers which came low over their stockings and garters. We were equipped—God knows by what scheming and stinting on mother's part—with Norfolk suits, starched Eton collars (with bows), bare knees, and roll-over stockings; and we'd no sooner step out of doors than the village boys would gather in force, shout insulting words, pelt us with balls of wet clay or fish-guts, and finally hide us: and mother was only persuaded to drop the collars because she got tired of washing the bloodstains from them. She held herself aloof from the village women, Down-Bank and Up-Bank. She flaunted the local feminine fashion. She detested the Bramblewick dialect (which in sheer self-defence we learnt to speak fluently), and we were punished if ever we came out with a 'thoo' or a 'summat', or a 'nowt'. It hurt her pride deeply that we had to go to the local elementary school. But by the time my brothers were old enough to leave she had saved enough from dad's summer visitor 'sales' to send them to a private school at Burnharbour, and as the saying goes, they had never 'looked back'. When my turn came to leave school she transcended this grand effort. A scholarship was offered in the new secondary school at S—. I had already made up my mind to go to sea, and I was relieved by my failure to please the examiners. Mother, mortified, but undismayed, promptly set off for the headquarters of the County Education Committee, interviewed the secretary, and procured within a week a special scholarship which put an end to my dreams of the Carribean Sea, and embroiled me (because of the school cap I had to wear) in a new series of bloody conflicts with the patriots, at a time when, by a courage at shouting rude remarks at strangers, and a fluency of bad language, I was acquiring a measure of tolerance, if not of popularity. . .

3

The north-east swell, which had depressed Marney Lunn, was still breaking across the landing mouth; but the tides were spring; and at low-water the scaurs which formed the landing would be bare, giving shelter to a narrow strip of deep water inside the breakers. This strip of water, particularly on a dark night, afforded excellent cod-fishing. You stood on the extremity of the west scaur, near the lowest of the marking posts—bare only at spring tides—and using a stout sea-rod, threw a weighted tackle to the margin of the breakers, where the fish lurked in the dense tangle of oar-weed. You leaned the rod against a stone then, to give its end a good upward slant, and you stood and waited, it might be a minute, it might be an hour, for the fierce jerk of a hooked fish. The village was half a mile landwards. Only the highest of its cottages, piled along the ridge of the sea-cliff, with a light gleaming here and there, were visible. North to Low Batts, south to High Batts, the scaurs made a series of flat, curving terraces, divided by quiet weedy lagoons until the tide rose, and the lines of surf pressed shorewards. You stood on a thick, squelching carpet of bladderwrack among which occasionally you caught the dull phosphorescent gleam of some creeping marine organism. On the calm surface of the water in the lee of the scaur, the fronds of oar-weed stirred gently, but farther out, where the seas were breaking, the weed forest rose and sank in sympathy with each incoming wave, with a deep breathing sound, following the crash of the wave itself as it split on the scaur ends.

That sound, in the darkness, the strong smell of weed and brine, the remoteness of the village, gave one a peculiar sense of intimacy with one's quarry. It was easy to imagine yourself passing between two elements which in the darkness were so much alike. You could move in the dark swaying forest of oar-weed, where your bait, a mussel, lay among the sunken rocks: and see perhaps a cod, with its body outlined in pale phosphorescence, nosing among the rocks for crabs or little fish or fat anemones. You could conjecture the cod's reactions to the mussel, suspicion, (a mussel sans shell), wise indifference, or unwise desire. You could, when the fish was hooked, comprehend its strategy by being yourself one moment, and being the cod the next, and by doing so mitigate your disappointment if he escaped, without spoiling your triumph if you landed him.

True, it was not so good to fish there by moonlight. Too much light made the fish shy. But to-night it looked as though the swell would have stirred up the sand, thickened the water enough to counter the light of the moon. There would be no harm in going down at low tide and trying for an hour. . . .

It would be a mistake, I thought, as I climbed down towards my buckets, to attempt to force the conception of this book. It was a fascinating theme; but I was not sure that my parents should be the prime movers in it. The same theme might be worked out with equal effectiveness, through the history of the Lunns, the surviving family of the Sledburgh invasion, who, after a period of seeming defeat, had recently given a new and virile challenge to the spirit of the place. There were other 'foreigners' who had discovered in Bramblewick that spirit of enmity: parsons, doctors, artists, tradesmen, a retired financier who wanted to build a promenade; a lady who, had run away from the Mormons, and had hanged herself one night in a cottage next to that which dad had converted into a studio. Most of these 'foreigners' (like the Mormon lady, but less dramatically) had made a speedy escape. A few had remained to a second generation. A few had propitiated the 'spirit', gone 'Bramblewick', and had been absorbed. But the Lunns were still fighting.

The cat, discouraged with its reconnaissance, but thinking I might have something to eat in the house, was waiting by the buckets; and it pleasantly fell in alongside me, so that its moon shadow, and mine, and the buckets', made a moving pattern on the turf which the patriots of Bramblewick had so often wet with my blood. I had nothing but a bowl of milk to offer, however, and it sour and with the cream skimmed off; and I had no sooner shut the door and set this bowl on the floor, than the cat was mewing to be back in the moonlight.

Yet it might have been the dust which cured its appetite, and the smell; for the kettle had capsized in the fireplace, extinguishing the fire, causing a new exudation of ashes, and filling the air with a steamy, sulphurous dust that was settling on everything and on no place more noticeably than the sheets of my unfinished pot-boiler. I relighted the fire, refilled the kettle, cleaned the hearth, and started to sweep the floor. By the time this was done, the kettle was boiling, and I opened the door next to the closet. Here was the scullery; really a vast cupboard lined with shelves, and with one large shelf for washing-up. The shelves contained an amazing collection of crockery; at least three dinner services, two tea services, many odd cups and saucers, and at least a score of jugs and bowls. Originally I had made a selection of just as many crocks as I should need for a single meal, with the idea that I should wash them immediately after use. But if the fire had gone out, leaving me no hot water, or I wanted to catch the tide for fishing; or Marney Lunn burst in on me with some exciting proposition; or I had a desire to work; the washing-up sometimes was postponed, bringing a new set of crocks into circulation; and for hygenic reasons I had substituted an alternative technique, a large bucket containing a 5 per cent solution of formaldehyde, in which the things could wait a more propitious occasion.

Given a good supply of boiling water, soap, a clean dry cloth, and no burnt saucepan or pudding dishes, washing-up is an agreeable occupation. There is, in the quick process of changing soiled dishes into clean ones, a rhythm which is very conducive to creative thought. While I washed up I went on thinking about my book.

It was to be a sincere and noble work of art. That theme, fascinating though it was, must be a slender framework only. Its subject was the place and its people. I wished to paint a four-dimensional picture of Bramble-wick; to make permanent the impressions I had absorbed during my childhood and youth. I wished to paint the true 'Bramblewicker', man and woman, Up-Bank, and Down-Bank, the old sea-captains, the ones still at sea; the ones who had made 'brass', the ones who hadn't. There was something magnificent in all these men. This pride of theirs, this enmity, was, I believed, a reflection of the pride and enmity of the sea, from which, generation after generation, they had fought for a livelihood. And the women had the same magnificence; a pride born from a conflict more hard for them because they fought passively. These people, and the fishermen, set against a background of the conflicting sea whose sound scarce ever left their ears, must dominate my picture.

I did not underrate the immensity of my task: nor was I, even while intoxicated by the easy rhythm of æsthetic achievement produced by the polishing of my clean hot plates, confidant of my ability to perform it. I was positive only of an immense potential creativeness within me, something explosive which still lacked the dynamic spark to set it off. I must wait for this. But as the fallow field stores energy for the coming crop, so must I go on absorbing Bramblewick. By talking 'Bramblewick', by doing (behind my mother's back) what Bramblewick did, I had as a boy in some measure got behind that subtle barrier of enmity. By talking 'Bramblewick' now, by 'going Bramblewick', by a more complete, yet curiously involuntary and agreeable process of propitiation, of surrender almost, I was reaching within this barrier again. I was not a startling foreigner to the place when I could empty my own ash buckets at the midden; or pick up firewood from the beach: or wear a guernsey and sea-boots: or if I helped the Lunns and the Fosdycks launch their cobles, and gut their fish: or go into the gas-house when the weather was cold, and warm my backside in front of the retorts, listening to and joining in with the local male gossipers. By living this life which came so easily to me, I was getting deeper and deeper into the atmosphere of what, when the inspiration came, I was going to write. But I reflected with a sudden dismay, that in the meantime I had to live, that I had a growing load of debts, and, until I finished and sold my pot-boiler, no money whatever. I glanced involuntarily from the pile of dry, clean dishes to the pages of the manuscript which I had piled on the table. I would start work in earnest as soon as I had cleared up the scullery.

I made a selection of a mug and two plates, and stacked the rest of the crockery on the shelves. The place had no sink. All waste liquids had to be dumped in the gutter at the street end. As I returned with my empty bucket, Mrs. Brewster passed me again. She had been down to the fish shop for the family supper of fried fish and chips. The scent of her packet reminded me that

I was hungry: but the sight of my clean crockery discouraged the thought of a meal. I lit a fag, sat down in the convertible bed-chair, and drew the pile of manuscript towards me. Immediately there were footsteps on the cobbled paving outside. The street door opened, and John Lunn (Marney's elder brother) stepped in, shutting the door behind him. He took a rather surprised glance round the room.

'Hello,' he said, 'have you been clearing up? It looks quite different somehow.'

With an easy swagger he walked forward, took a fag from the tin on the mantelpiece, then cleared a space for himself on the settee, and sat down.

'I'm not going to stay long' he explained, reaching his feet towards the fire. 'Supper will be ready in a few minutes. I thought I'd just look in and ask your opinion about something. Aye, about an idea I've got.'

Despite that he affected a certain gloominess of attitude towards the smaller things of life, and that he suffered from an unevenness of temper, due possibly to the fact that he was unmated, John Lunn, I thought, succeeded as a man. He had a fair conceit, but it was healthy. When he was 'washed and dressed' (as he was at present), with a new guernsey on, and a white silk scarf just showing above his collar, I had observed that he liked to take a glance at himself in a looking-glass: and I regretted that among the articles I had stowed in the closet was an oval mirror in a fumed oak frame, which had hung over the mantelpiece in a light which would have shown John to himself, at his best. He had a broad, almost Dutch type of face, with a fair skin (still sunburnt), and fair, wavy hair (he was certainly proud of his hair), and a big mouth with strong teeth. It was an honest face, with plenty of character in it, some obstinacy at the corners of the mouth, but real strength and determination in the nose and chin; and in his blue eyes was a dour humour and imagination. He had conceit. He could be stupidly dogmatic and loquacious. But what I liked about his conceit was that it was little more than an out-size garment on his genuine character, and that where it bulged it hid a weakness that was better hidden.

I encouraged him by pushing away the pages of manuscript.

'I'm not stopping you from doing anything important, am I?' he inquired politely, at the same time methodically lighting his fag.

I assured him that he was not, and asked him what his idea was.

He at once took up a semi-defiant attitude.

'I reckon you'll laugh at it,' he said, 'same as father did. I've just been having a hell of an argument with father, as a matter of fact. He says you can't start anything new in Bramblewick. He says you can talk about it, and get chaps to agree with you, and promise, but it all comes to nowt in the end. . . . Well, I reckon it's just daftness talking like that. What he can't see is that things change. Bramblewick's a different spot to what it was when he first came here. It's changed to my knowledge, particularly since the war. There's wireless for one thing, and the Burnharbour bus, which lets folk go to the pictures. I tell you Bramblewick people are getting their minds broadened. But you can't get father to see it, I'm damned if you can.'

I knew better than try to hurry John. He had a gift for talking, and a strong dramatic instinct. He preferred the roundabout route to a point.

'Of *course* Bramblewick folk are getting their minds broadened,' he went on. 'It stands to reason they are. Before the war the only music they had a chance of hearing was what they got at church or chapel, and the choral society, or twice a year when they got a brass band to play at the Shepherds' and Oddfellows' walks. I reckon that now, with almost everyone listening in, they've got to know what real music is. They're learning to appreciate it. And I mean real music, not just singing and piano. Bands. Aye, *bands*.'

John repeated that last word with an emphasis which gave me a first clue to his 'idea'.

'Bands,' he repeated again. And then, with a dramatic gesture of his hand, a conductor's gesture almost, he demanded:

'Why can't Bramblewick have a band of its own?'

He answered that question immediately.

'There's no reason why it can't. There's not many young chaps knocking about the place, I'll admit, but there's enough to make a band. There's most of them would be only too glad to learn an instrument, particularly in winter when there's nowt else to do. Take a night like this for example. There's the billiard room, we know, but with only one table, and all those old retired skippers from Up-Bank playing their hundreds up, and thinking themselves champions if they make a break of ten, how long have you to wait for a game?

Choir practices are all right, but they're only once a week, and you get sick of only hymns. Now with a band you could play what you had a mind to learn: marches, waltzes, bits out of opera, popular songs, things like "Annie Laurie" and "Killarney", anything. There was a brass band on the wireless the other night. A colliery band. God—it was champion! It almost made tears come into your eyes when they played "Londonderry Air". And only a colliery band, mind you. Only miners. Working-class people, same as us.'

John again made that dramatic gesture.

'Is there any real reason why some of us shouldn't get together, and start a Bramblewick Brass Band. It only wants a start. We'd get up a dance to open a fund for buying instruments. We'd get the M.P. and the Liberal candidate, aye, perhaps even the Labour candidate, to give us subscriptions. There's several people Up-Bank who might help. . . . Now what do you think of it— candidly. You know as much about Bramblewick as any of us?'

I did so. I was thinking swiftly of the Bramblewick Golf Club, whose pavilion this last fifteen years had been a store shed for a local mason; of dad's Miniature Rifle Range, now used as a hen-house by some farmer up the Dale; of the Bramblewick Amateur Dramatic Society, the Bramblewick Physical Culture Class, the Bramblewick Football Club; and, most ill-fated venture of all, the No. I Bramblewick Troop of Boy Scouts, of which I was the organizer, the Scoutmaster, and, after the first parade, the one scout, a solitary, disillusioned Lone Scout, with my shirt in ribbons, and gory, my scout's hat ruined by being kicked round the Dock by the patriots, and my scout's badge of a fleur-de-Iys bearing that ironic legend BE PREPARED, a crumpled piece of metal.

I believed that (provided you were a 'foreigner') John's father was right. A 'foreigner' could not start anything new in Bramblewick and prosper with it. Wherever you turned, for sympathy or support you would find that enmity, as powerful to-day, as it had been in my childhood. But I saw no reason to present this view-point to John.

I told him I thought the Bramblewick Brass Band a fine idea. If there was anything I could do (apart from being an actual member of the band) he could count on me. I might even subscribe, when I got hold of some money. But in the look John gave me, as he got up, there was a vague suspicion; and he said with a slow lugubriousness:

'Aye. Well, I don't pretend it's going to be an easy job. It's raising the brass that will be the hardest part of it. But it's time something was done to liven this spot up in winter. I sometimes wish I was out of it, back at sea. It's not so bad when you're fishing. But when you get day after day of bad weather, and there's nowt to do, it gets on your nerves. . . Listen to that bloody sea roaring now. It never leaves off. It's as though it was laughing at you. . . . Well, I'll get home, or I'll be late for supper. Have you had yours yet? You'd better come along if you haven't.'

I told John that I was going to work. He moved to the door, and turning with his hand on it, said thoughtfully:

'He's a queer chap, our old man. To hear him talk you'd think he was as old fashioned as anyone in

Bramblewick. Yet what do you think he was doing when I left him? He'd got an old lobster pot set in front of the fire; and he was sitting there, just staring at it, and trying to think out how he can make a lobster-pot that will shut up, so that you can stow a lot of them in a coble at once.'

'It's not a bad idea, of course,' John continued, 'if it could be done. He reckons that lobster fishing is about the only paying thing left for small chaps like us. It would mean that you could carry six times as many pots as you can do ordinary ones; so that if you were caught with them in shallow water with a sudden breeze, you could rush them out to deep water in one trip, or even bring them ashore, and not have them smashed up, same as happened to us three times last season. They cost a lot to make, do lobster pots, apart from your time. Thousands of pounds' worth go west every year along this coast. Aye, and on other coasts too, not only England either! Why, if you reckoned France, and Norway, and Canada, and the States, it would come to hundreds of thousands of pounds' worth of gear lost every year. In a few years' time it would amount to *millions!* Just swallowed up by the sea! And most of that would be saved if you could make a pot that would shut up when you wanted it shut up, and fish as well as other pots when it wasn't. I should think there's a fortune waiting the chap who could invent a shut-up lobster pot and put it on the market at a reasonable price.'

John opened the door.

'Well, if you won't come to supper, I'll say so long!'

He stepped out. The street door slammed behind him. Without guessing what a desperate infection he had put into my blood, I drew the manuscript towards me again, and stared into the fire while his footsteps grew fainter and fainter until they were lost in the muffled roar of the sea. Then I selected from the pile the sheet I had been working on last, read through what I had written, and tried to concentrate my mind on the task of continuation. But there was something restless and exciting in the sound of the surf, and before I had made any practical progress my mind was wandering. Soon there were footsteps on the cobbles again. The door opened, and Marney Lunn stepped in. Like John, he had his moment of surprise.

'God!' he cried. 'You've had a rare tidying up!'

Like John, he swaggered over to the fireside and took a fag. Like John, he would have liked that mirror to have been there; for he had John's good looks, John's self-confidence, John's wholesome conceit. But he did not sit down. He said confidently, and in a way that brooked no refusal:

'Come on, look lively. Amy's just put that fish in the pan and she's laid supper for three. You know what she's like if she's kept waiting. Come on!'

4

Fishing that night at the mouth of Bramblewick Landing, I had made a peculiar catch.

The wind had dropped to a miraculous calm. Inside the loud sounding surf, between the sheltering scaur ends, the Landing was smooth and polished under the brilliant light of the moon. I had fished for an hour without success, when, proceeding to haul in my line to see if the bait was intact, I felt a powerful resistance. At first I thought it was a large crab, but when I had reeled in a yard or two, there was an unmistakable wriggle and tug.

I knew by experience that it was not a cod. The weight and the repeated tugs suggested a conger: and, mindful of the oar-weed, through which the sunken tackle had to pass before it reached the scaur, I began to reel in furiously, hoping to bring my quarry to the surface, and thus avoid entanglement.

Suddenly, about fifteen yards out from where I stood there was a splash and a gleam, such as the white belly of a large fish would make in the moonlight. My rod was now bent in an exciting bow: the strain on it was so great that I had a quick doubt as to my wisdom in making a direct landing. I eased the strain therefore. The gleaming object sank out of sight.

More cautiously now, I reeled in, and glanced round

at my gaff in preparation for the final struggle when the fish broke water within range.

Was it a conger, or a very large flat-fish? Again I caught the gleam of white down in the water, and not more than ten feet away. Checking the reel, I elevated my rod tip, until I got the full strain. The fish broke surface into the full light of the moon. I saw that it was no fish at all, but an old, battered, yet still in places immaculately white enamel chamber pot, hooked by the handle. The body of the pot, forming an unsteady sea-anchor, had produced the drag, and the very life-like tugs.

I met Marney Lunn after dinner. He had suggested that if the sea was rough, we should go into the country, and cut hazels for lobster pots. The wind had risen at dawn, and was blowing a half gale from the north-east, when we walked along the shore to Garry Beck, from whose Cove our road led inland. Marney was impressed by the story of my night's adventure.

'God!' he remarked. 'It's just as though the sea was playing a joke on you. It's just as though someone was spitting in your face. The sea's done nowt but play one long joke on us this autumn,' he went on, scowling at the lines of breakers roaring in to the shore. 'Look how the wind dropped last night. You could have sworn it would have been fishing weather to-day. And look at it now!'

The tide was flowing. Only a narrow strip of shingle remained between its margin and the foot of the boulder clay cliff, which reaches south from the village to Garry Beck. At Garry Beck a shaley bluff, known as the Nab, projecting fifty feet from the line of cliff, makes the shore impassable long before the tide is full. A flat scaur skirts the foot of the Nab. The sea was breaking over the deep outer edge of this, and yellow spume blew in our faces as we crossed it.

'I never come round Garry Beck Nab, in wild weather,' said Marney, 'without thinking of poor Jack Sayers. Talk about the sea playing jokes! It played one on that chap and no mistake.'

'That chap hated the sea,' Marney went on, as, reaching the Cove, we turned our backs against the wind, and climbed up a bank of shingle and weed, to the lane leading up the south side of Garry Dale. 'He hated it. He liked horses, and messing about with farmers, in spite that his father was a sea-captain, and nearly all his relations were sailors. Jack always had an idea that he'd be drowned if he went to sea, although he'd never flinch at jumping a hedge or even a stream, and was as good a chap on horseback as there's ever been round here. And fancy him going the way he did. Can you remember it?'

It was Bramblewick history, but I liked the sound of Marney's voice and his way of telling a yarn so I said nothing. The lane climbed steeply between withered straggling hedges of briar and thorn, beaded with scarlet berries. To our left was a rough bank, patched with dead bracken and tousely whins, and to our right we looked down on Garry Beck and the old Mill, and we were level with the tree tops of Garry Wood, from which the north-easter was tearing the last of the dead leaves, and piling them in thick heaps upon the undergrowth. Dark clouds swept in a torrent overhead. The noise of the sea pursued us.

'Aye,' Marney continued. 'The sea played a joke on

poor Jack Sayers, and no mistake. Jack was one of the nicest chaps that ever came out of Bramblewick. You'd never hear a word said against him. But he'd never had very good health, and he was very quiet, and he had some queer ideas. He had a dread of being suffocated: couldn't bear being shut up anywhere; and he often said that when he died he wanted a glass window put in his coffin lid for fear that if he wasn't really dead, he could let folks know, and save him from being buried. But more than anything he was afraid of the sea. That was queer; for his father had done well out of it; made as much brass as any of those Up-Bank skippers. If Jack had gone to sea, he'd have been certain of a ship the day he got his ticket. But there you are! He was afraid of it, and he liked the feel of a horse's reins, just as some chaps like the feel of a boat's sheets, or a tiller in their hands; and he never went to sea at all, and used to spend all his time riding and fox-hunting. But Jack's father was that fond of him, he could have done anything he liked. They say that if he had asked for a stable full of horses he could have had them. And I reckon that's queer, too. Most of those Up-Bank skippers would have played hell with their sons, if they hadn't wanted to go to sea.'

Marney crouched into the hedge to light a fag. Then:

'I was only a kid, but I remember that day as though it was only last week; and it was in winter time, too. Hounds were to meet at High Batts top, about eleven o'clock. The tide would be about half ebb in the morning, and Jack would get round Garry Nab easily. The meet was at the pub, but before they made a start, the wind freshened south-west, and it began raining. Most of them gave it up straight away. But some stayed on, thinking it might clear up, and they'd get a bit of sport. And it wasn't until it was nearly dark that they gave it up altogether, and started for home. Jack was the only Bramblewick chap left. He could have come back round the country, of course, but he reckoned the tide wouldn't be quite up to the Nab, and that meant saving at least four miles. So he chanced it!'

We had reached the top of Garry Dale. Our lane led due west, across level farmlands, but to our left we had a view of the shoulder of High Batts, and the south corner of the Bay, which, completely exposed, was feeling the full force of the growing storm. From the inn at the top of High Batts, a rough bridle track skirts the moor, then branches down to Browe Beck — a stream flowing into the Bay a mile farther south than Garry — and to the shore. But there is no projecting scaur at Browe Beck. One can make the passage as far as Garry Beck even at high water of a neap tide: and local farmers, rather than take the long inland route will wade their horses round the Nab if the water is not more than girth deep, and there is no surf.

'It was a hell of a night,' Marney went on. 'The wind backed. It would be blowing east, straight off the sea, by five o'clock; and it doesn't take more than an hour for an easterly wind to raise a swell. Aye, and an easterly wind will bring the tide in quicker, too. I reckon myself it must have been that what put him wrong when he got to the Nab. It would be pitch dark by then, and raining like hell. Jack wouldn't have tried wading round if he'd thought the water was deep. He was too afraid of the sea for that.

39

There mightn't have been very much water really. But a wave might have rushed over the scaur edge, and knocked the horse off its feet, throwing Jack overboard, and sucking him back over the scaur. But no one knew exactly what had happened, and no one ever will. Folks that went out to look for him found his horse up near the Mill Dam, shaking with cold and fright. But there was no sign of Jack.'

'Aye, the sea had got him,' Marney added slowly, and with a peculiar reverence, as though he spoke of the sea as a god. 'It had got him, after all. They dragged the mill dam; but it seems he wasn't meant to be drowned in fresh water. When the sea calmed boats went out, and grappled Garry Sands, and shot salmon nets across the scaur ends, thinking they might catch him. On the tenth night, when they expected him to float, all Bramblewick was out on the scaurs at low tide. There were lanterns and torches everywhere, from Low Batts to High Batts. It looked as though all the stars had fallen out of the sky into the sea, for it was a pitch dark night. But his body must have got buried in that patch of mud that lies off Garry Beck, or got caught among the tangles. It wasn't until another north-easter came that it shifted and washed ashore, just north of the Nab. Poor Jack! Fancy him being afraid of being suffocated, and hating the sea like he did, and then being drowned from a horse's back. But his father gave him his wish. He had a little porthole put in his coffin lid, only it was covered up with flowers.'

We walked on, with the cold sea wind, and the sound of the sea pursuing us. We passed a farmstead on our right, and a little farther on, a man ploughing, with a flock of herring gulls following close to the plough, and squabbling fiercely over the rare worms turned out of the hard, wind-dried soil. The man was old and thin and dejected looking. Occasionally he had to leave go of the plough handles to beat the circulation back into his hands. Marney gave him a commiserating glance as we passed.

'Say what you like,' he said. 'I wouldn't be a farmer. It may be safer. You get a bigger chance of dying in your bed. But who the hell wants to die in a bed, and have a lot of folks fussing about, pretending to be sorry for you, when all the time they're looking forward to the funeral, as if they were going to the pictures, and someone else was paying for their seats. I'd hate to be a farmer. Look at that poor devil, walking up and down that field from morn till night, and nothing to show for it when it's finished, but a lot of sods turned the other way up. We know that farming's not all ploughing. But there's not much variety in it. One turnip's like any other turnip; and a crop of corn always comes up pretty much the same as the crop before it.'

'Of course,' Marney went on, after a thoughtful silence during which he took what seemed like a surreptitious glance over his shoulder at the sea, 'I'll not say that fishing can't break a man's heart. When you spend months, and a hell of a lot of brass making fleets of lobster pots, and you see them all smashed up the first day you put them in the sea, it doesn't do your temper any good. Then take cod: you've got to buy bait, and pay a big price for it. You've got to bait your lines the day before you go fishing, and if it's bad weather, and goes on being bad weather, your bait rots and rusts the hooks, and it's all got to be taken off again, and fresh bait put on in case you do get fair weather. On top of that fish are scarcer, because of the steam trawlers coming close in and killing all the young fish. There's plenty of chaps along the coast who've had their hearts broken by fishing since the war. Hundreds of them up north have gone into the iron mines and steel works, and left fishing altogether. The truth is, there's only one sort of fishing that's any use to chaps like us, and that's lobsters. But you want a big boat for a game like that to make big money at it. You want a lot of pots, and be able to take the lot of them on board at one go, if you're fishing close in, and it comes on bad weather. Apart from lobstering, there's scarcely a living in inshore fishing, these days.'

I knew about the desperate depression which had befallen the craft of inshore fishing along the northeast coast since the war. There was not a fishing village between the Humber and the Tees which had not suffered. There could be no doubt that the inshore fisherman's grounds had been ruined by intensive close in trawling, for at Bramblewick in my own memory, the average catch of a boat for a day's fishing had dropped from as many as twenty baskets to three. It was not that steam trawlers fishing along the legal three-mile limit (and frequently inside it) made such big hauls. Their marketable catches were negligible compared with the wholesale slaughter of immature fish which is inevitable when a trawl is dragged across what is virtually a nursery ground. Again, the cost of the inshore fisherman's bait, of his gear, his boats—their tackle and cost of maintenance—had more than doubled: and of late years the growing economic depression had decreased the demand for fish, establishing it as a luxury, without however conferring on the fisherman the benefit of a luxury price.

During the brief period of prosperity in the iron and steel industry of the Tees which had followed the war, there had been a strong demand for unskilled labour. Hundreds of young fishermen (most of them just demobilized from the navy) had been attracted by the good wages, and the prospect of steady employment. And now that a slump had attacked these industries, they had returned to their villages, where, without the capital necessary to embark on the gamble of fishing, they had been forced on to the dole.

True that at Bramblewick the situation was materially different. The rot had set in long before the war. Either the old fishing families had died out, or the younger generation of them inspired by the growing rows of Up-Bank villas, had entered the mercantile marine. The Fosdycks, Luke and Tindal, had remained faithful to their craft, and were still fishing. But even the Lunn boys, John and Marney, had gone to sea, while their father, Henry, after the return of the Sledburgh 'foreigners' to their native village, had gone into partnership in a deep sea boat, operating from the larger fishing ports of the coast. When the partnership had been dissolved at the end of the war, Henry had been obliged to take a shore job at Bramblewick; and it was only a year or two ago that John and Marney had given up the sea, and joined their father in a small motor coble, which they were now operating.

Henry Lunn had detested that job ashore; although it was well paid, and offered him permanent employment and security for the rest of his life. I believed that for him it symbolized defeat in his long struggle against the Fosdycks and Bramblewick. He was by tradition and choice an inshore fisherman. He was never happy except in a boat. It must have been for him an almost unendurable exasperation, to watch the Fosdycks at work in the Bay, and himself without even a small boat to 'go off' in: and I believed that in giving up the mercantile marine, both John and Marney had been moved chiefly by an affection and loyalty towards their father; but that in them also was a sense of the same old conflict.

Would Bramblewick beat the Lunns as it had beaten the rest of the Sledburgh 'foreigners'? Was this merely a temporary fed-uppishness of Marney's, or was it the expression of a deeper discouragement?

We walked on in silence for a time. The lane now slanted to the south, and was bringing us to the edge of Browe Beck Dale, and the wooded gorge through which the beck runs down from the moor. We could still feel the full force of the wind, but the trees in the gorge escaped its withering blast, and were not yet despoiled of their autumn splendour. They were oaks, chiefly; but an odd beech and ash added splashes of deep red, and ochre, and brown to the dominant note of pale terra cotta, and there were the dark evergreens of spruce and holly. High up the gorge, where the stream bit deeply into the black moor edge, were the copses of hazel for which we were bound.

'Mind, I'm not saying that we've got much cause for croaking,' said Marney at last. 'We've had our ups and downs since we started fishing again. We've lost a lot of gear, but we've had some spells of good luck, and we've made a lot of brass at times; enough to save us from starvation, anyway. It's line fishing that's lets us down. Last year we didn't average more than five bob a week each the whole winter, and it looks like being worse this winter, with cod the price it is. If only we could go on fishing for lobsters! If only we could take pots with us in the coble as we take our lines, and bring them home every night, so as to have them safe! There's plenty of lobsters about until the end of November. Think of the price they'd bring, with no one else fishing. But this time of year you daren't leave them in the sea at night, and it takes us all our time to launch the cobles up and down without carrying heavy, clumsy things like pots.'

'Father's trying to work out a new sort of lobster pot by the way,' Marney went on. 'One that shuts up. He thinks that if it would work we'd be able to fish for lobsters in winter. According to our John, he was at it all last evening, making a hell of a mess, in front of the kitchen fire, and no one could get a word out of him. But he hadn't got much further with it when I saw him this morning. He was in one of his bad moods, grumpy as hell. I told him it only wanted an hour's north-easterly swell to shut up a lobster pot, anyway, and his job was to make it stand up again after the sea had done with it. But I'm damned if he could see the joke. Now I reckon it wants someone with a brain like yours to invent a thing like that.'

Marney had a habit of leg-pulling, and, suspecting irony in the last remark, I retaliated by asking him if he had heard if anyone else in the village had sent in correct solutions to the cross-word puzzle.

'Aye,' he answered, rather sadly. 'From what I've heard half of Bramblewick must have had a go at that competition, and everyone I've spoken to seems to have filled it in the same way as we did. I reckon there's a trick in it somewhere. I shouldn't be surprised if no one gets a penny out of it.'

Clearly the subject of cross-word puzzles, with their easy gold, had ceased to interest Marney, for he said in the same breath, and very seriously:

'You know there's no doubt that a shut-up pot would be a God-send to inshore fishermen like us. It would mean you could fish at least two months longer into the back-end of the year; and it would save thousands of pounds worth of gear being lost. It would mean, too, that you could go off into deep water, and find grounds that never had been fished; for you could stow them, so that your boat would be safe in any sort of weather. I've thought a lot about it myself, since father had the idea, but I can't see how it can be done. Not a pot that you can shut up, and then open again when you want to fish with it. Can you?'

I had to confess to Marney that I had only the vaguest idea as to how a lobster pot was constructed. I knew, of course, that it was made of boards and hazel hoops covered with netting, and provided with net funnels by which lobsters entered. I had some idea, too, of the immense amount of labour that went into construction; and the Bramblewick lobster season was always connected in my mind with those periodic catastrophes when the potters were caught close in by a north-easter, and the beach next day was strewn with the wreckage of pots and tangled ropes. But my interest in fishing had been chiefly an angler's interest. I had never conceived any excitement in the setting and hauling of pots, and therefore I had never troubled to examine one except casually.

Even now I felt no deep conscious interest in this project of a 'shut-up' pot. I was concerned only with a growing conviction that Marney, usually the most hopeful of men was more than temporarily disgusted with his job, and that the whole family was under the strain of threatened defeat. They had thrown up good jobs to start fishing again. They had invested a good lump of their savings in their motor coble and fishing gear. It would be a humiliating surrender to 'Bramblewick' if they had to abandon fishing and leave the place for ever.

Marney, however, soon cheered up. The lane forked, and we took the branch which led south, down into the valley of Browe Beck. A dense tangle of whins and bramble on our left broke the force of the wind. We had a smell that was not that of the sea; but of wet earth, and cattle dung, and decaying leaves. The sound of the sea became a murmur. As though for the first time, we heard the lowing of cattle from a farm up near the moor edge; the sharp bark of a dog, a man's voice. Two magpies were chattering in the brambles. Down by the beck a carrion crow croaked noisily; and a flock of starlings suddenly flew over our heads so close that we heard the whirr of their quick wings.

For the time being we both forgot the sea. We had an obliterating sense of land. Although the sky was still obscured by grey windy clouds, the atmosphere was clear, the light strong, and the trees by the beck and up the gorge made a violent contrast of colour against the faded green of the lower pastures, and the dark escarpment of the moors. Our eyes were drawn to the trees as a child's eyes are drawn to a fire. They seemed to exude a physical warmth.

'God, it's champion!' Marney muttered. 'It's as good as a picture. You know I'm not very fond of the country as a rule, but I reckon this is one of the prettiest spots there is round Bramblewick. It's a pity we're too late for brambles though,' he added, more practically, and with a sudden glance at the thicket, 'but we might get a few nuts where we're going, if the squirrels haven't eaten them. Anyway I'm going to take back a sprig or two of beech leaves for Amy. They'll look champion on the mantelpiece in a vase.'

There was a wooden footbridge across the Beck, and a deep overgrown pool below it. We halted here, looking at the pool, for it was a favourite lurking place for salmon trout in autumn. But I soon found myself thinking not of salmon trout, but of how I had once stood on this bridge on a certain warm June night with a girl whose name, appropriately, was Eve. We were both sixteen. She was not Bramblewick, however. She carne from Manchester, and she was staying with some 'foreign folk' who had a holiday cottage, Down Bank. She was dark and slender and pretty, and was dressed in what was then regarded as scandalous by the villagers, a hobble skirt with a smart coat, and a low, white silk blouse, and the shiniest of black silk stockings, with high-heeled shoes. I could scarcely believe it possible that so ravishing a creature could smile at me. I don't know how many times we passed each other on the beach (Bramblewick's summer promenade) before I was sufficiently emboldened to speak to her. But that brave act achieved, Eve quickly cured my boyish shyness, and thrilled me to the marrow, by asking me if I knew of any nice walks round Bramblewick; she was so bored by the beach and her friends didn't like walking; and, she daren't go by herself because she was afraid of tramps and bulls, and dogs and things like that, and getting lost. She wouldn't be afraid of going anywhere with me though. I looked so strong, and she just knew she could trust me.

I believed that I had found in Eve my ideal of womanhood. She was lovelier than any of the Harrison Fisher girls on the covers of *Nash's Magazine.* I discovered in a week, during which we rambled over the whole of Fylingdales, that she was interested in all the things that interested me. She told me that she loved to hear me talk; she loved to have me show her things, like birds' nests and fossils, and tadpoles, and the tumuli on Browe Moor, and rare flowers and curious insects. She was so glad I was not like some boys, who only wanted to kiss and be sloppy. She hated that sort of thing! And in all that time I never misinterpreted the simple trust with which she

49

put her hand in mine when I was helping her across a stream, or the way she clutched my arm when we met some cattle. She inspired me to such a purity of mind that once when she broke a suspender getting over a fence, I walked on nearly a quarter of a mile, in the manner of Lot, never once looking back, until she rejoined me.

We came to the bridge on our way back from the moors. The air was warm and scented with hay, and honeysuckle, and whin blossom. The moon had risen above the ridge of the moor. We stopped in the middle of the bridge (exactly where Marney and I stood now), leaning with our backs against the hand-rail, looking down into the pool where the moon made a shivering reflection. I wanted to tell Eve how I had once seen a salmon there, and how I had nearly caught it, but she stopped me with a whispered 'hush' . We were silent, and there was no sound but the beck. Then I became frightened. I could not take my eyes from the reflection of the moon. I felt that I was being hypnotized, that a horrible spell was coming over me. My knees trembled. I tried to speak and could not get my breath. Then Eve touched my hand with hers, clutched it. Her legs touched mine. I felt the heat of flesh through her skirt. I gasped. I felt her turning towards me. I tried to move away, but instead, as though she were a magnet, and my body iron, I turned to her, and our bodies touched, the whole length of them, and I was looking into her face, which she had thrown back, so that the moon made a dull fire in her eyes. Then slowly she moved her face nearer. Our cheeks touched. I made an awkward unsuccessful effort to find her mouth. She laughed, softly, mockingly. And with that something went bang inside me. I put my arms fiercely round her waist and shoulder. I crushed her with all my strength, and with my eyes closed I kissed her.

On the way home I asked Eve if she would be my wife. She said that she would. We both realized, however, that marriage was not practical until we were older, and I was earning a large enough salary to provide her with a home; and we agreed that for the present we should keep our engagement secret from our parents. We swore eternal fidelity to each other. When she returned to Manchester (the thought of that impending separation brought a lump to my throat), we would write every day. I told Eve that from now on I would have one thought, to make a success of my life for her sake. Next term at school I would work hard, and although I was still uncertain as to whether I should be a ship's captain, or a distinguished scientist, or go in for art, I was confident that in a few years I should be earning a pretty decent salary, enough at least for us to marry and have our first child, a boy.

Eve left Bramblewick three days later. The same night I composed a poem in blank verse in which I expressed my anguish at seeing her train climb round the moor edge and finally disappear into the mouth of High Batts tunnel, leaving behind it a cloud of steam which swirled into thin wisps among the heather and whins, and quickly became nothing. I called it 'The Tunnel', and I was so impressed by it that I decided that I would become a poet. But I did not guess how apt was the symbolism of my poem; what an exact analogy there was between that dissipating cloud of steam and Eve. I sent her the poem and a long letter next day, and a letter every day for a week. She sent me nothing. Years after I heard by chance that she had married the manager of a multiple store shop in Salford, and that she had got several children.

'I don't think there's a fish there to-day,' said Marney. 'When it's dull like this they always lie at this end of the pool.'

'Aye,' I said, tearing myself from the memory of that glamorous summer night. 'I once saw one like that, a long time ago. I crept down under the bridge, and got my hands on it, but it was too slippery, and got away.'

'You ought to have got your fingers into its gills, that's the only way to hold a live fish. . . . Come on, we mustn't forget those hazels. And I've got to get a sprig of beech leaves for Amy, remember.'

It did not take us long to reach the copse where (in return for a promised boiling of crabs) Marney had leave from a farmer to cut hazels. Here we were in the wind again, and we had a view across the valley and the fields beyond of the north end of the bay, with the roofs of the village making a red blur in the mist which the breakers were now throwing up along the whole coastline. The wind seemed to be increasing in force. It was bitterly cold. Marney pulled out his knife as we forced our way through the thick undergrowth towards the first clump of hazels.

I had imagined that cutting hazels was a very simple, easy task. I was surprised first to find that in a clump containing perhaps a score of apparently good sticks only two or three came within Marney's definition of what a 'pot hazel' should be. They had to be straight, about an inch in diameter at the base, at least a yard long, and without flaw. I learnt next that even with a sharp knife the wood was extraordinarily tough, and that while it was easy enough to bend a stick down and cut it at the bend, this resulted in a split, and spoilt it. The twigs on each stick were equally tough. As many as a dozen of these had to be removed cleanly before the stick was done. Three hazels were required for the hoops of one pot, Marney informed me. You had to allow one extra for being broken during the bending process, and another for making the three straight thinner lengths of the frame.

'Aye, and we're going to make over a hundred pots this winter,' he informed me further. 'Lobsters are our only hope for making up what we lose on cod. We can only fish ninety from our coble, but we've got to reckon on losing at least half of them, in the early part of the season, so we've got to have the others in reserve, so as not to stop us fishing when prices are good. We want at least five hundred hazels, and that won't be enough if we have a run of bad luck.'

I was at work on my second stick, and already my hands were sore from the friction of my knife handle. When it was done, I found myself looking almost involuntarily towards the distant roaring sea, and thinking how for generations the laborious business of making lobster pots had gone on, not only at Bramblewick, but along the whole coast, and how the sea had gone on destroying. There was a reward, for men had got their living from the inshore sea. But it seemed that in the long conflict between the two, the sea had

53

maintained an increasing advantage. It was perhaps in effect, an economic advantage. Other factors than the destructiveness of the sea were playing their part in this slow but certain extinction of a tribe of fine men. Science and the capitalist had produced the steam trawler, spoiler of the inshore grounds; but more deadly because of its range and independence of the weather. The inshore fisherman's catch was small, uncertain, and expensively produced. He had no transport or selling organization. He was at the mercy of the middleman.

I could see the force of Marney's contention, that in lobster fishing lay his last hope for existence, for the lobster's favourite habitat is rough, rocky ground where the trawler dare not venture its gear. The most effective means of catching lobsters was still the primitive pot, but against this had to be measured the recurring and seemingly inevitable loss of gear. The entire profit of a season might easily be wiped out in one destructive storm.

Was this loss inevitable, I suddenly wondered? If it was due to the fragility of the lobster pot, was it impossible to design and construct a trap for lobsters that would withstand the buffetings of storm and tide? Science had made the petrol engine available to the inshore fisherman. Very few sailing cobles were now left along the coast. Surely science could produce something to replace the primitive, costly, laboriously made, and yet so easily destructible lobster pot, and thus help the fisherman in his last desperate struggle against extinction.

Marney himself was at work only on his fourth hazel.

'You know,' I said, 'what you chaps ought to have is a lobster pot that won't smash up in bad weather. Have you ever thought of having them made with an iron frame instead of hazel and wood?'

'Garn,' Marney replied without taking his attention from his task, 'it would cost too much brass, and even if it was made of armour plate it wouldn't stand up against a north-easter. If you want to know what the sea can do to iron, go and have a look at one of those old wrecks along High Batts. You'll see sheets of steel buckled and torn like cardboard; and a propeller shaft bent like a candle on a hot night. Besides you couldn't make a pot like ours out of metal. Not one that would fish as well. I've seen lobsters caught all over the world, in Canada and the States, in Norway and France, and other parts of England, but I've never yet seen a pot to fish as well as ours.'

'They're queer things, are lobsters,' Marney went on as he threw the finished hazel on one side, and knelt down to cut another, 'they're very fastidious. They'll make as much fuss going into a pot as an old maid will getting into bed, when she thinks there might be a man hiding under the mattress. Everything's got to be just right for them. Bait's got to be neither too fresh, nor too stale, there mustn't be any crabs inside first, there mustn't be anything to frighten them, like a bit of loose ballast, or a frayed rope-end flapping in the tide. A lobster won't go into a pot if there's any white paint on the bottom boards. We used a bit of iron drain pipe for ballast in a pot once. That pot never caught a lobster until we took the pipe out. The tide must have whistled through it and frightened them. No, if you come out fishing with us a few times when we start lobstering, you'll have to agree that you can't beat our pots for fishing. But I still think they'd be more useful if you could shut them up, without making them different.'

I said no more; but I resolved that I should have a good look at a pot when we got home. I cut another hazel and trimmed it. We moved on to another clump. The light was now perceptibly failing. The glowing colours of the wood beneath us made a less startling contrast against the pastures; and to the north-east, the low flying clouds and the sea, and the cliffs beyond the village were merging in an homogenous grey. It was hard work, yet soon I was aware of a peculiar satisfaction in finding a good stick, in deciding from its rich brown, shiny, mottled bark that it was living wood, flawless, and of the right length; in hacking my way through it, and finally throwing it clean, on to the pile. The smells were the smells of land, but the tang of brine was in the wind. From the farm came the sound of cattle being herded into the milking shed; but one never lost sound of the sea; and it seemed to me that there was something warlike and challenging in that sound which gave a warlike significance to our task, as though we were making weapons.

We had cut about forty hazels when Marney took a piece of rope from his pocket, and we started to collect them, and tie them into faggots.

'I promised Amy I wouldn't be late for tea,' he said. 'It will take us a good hour to get home, with the tide up. Remind me about those beech leaves when we get down to the beck.'

The beech leaves, with a spray of scarlet hips, to 'brighten them up,' were duly collected before we crossed the bridge of my glamorous memory. From here to Garry Beck Cove we retraced our outward route. From the Cove we were obliged to climb to the top of the clay cliff, and follow a rough path along its edge towards the village. Dusk was falling. Westwards the land was obscure. The gale-torn surf, however, gave a peculiar light, like that of a snow-field, to the sea itself, and the sweeping cliffs of the bay were sharply defined against a continuous ribbon of churned up water made by the collision of the incoming breakers with the backwash of the broken waves that preceded them. A deep, steady thunder filled the air. Yet above this we heard the direct impact of seas launching themselves against the foot of the crumbling cliff below us, the thud of tumbling earth and clay, the awful rasping suck of the backwash, carrying away its spoil, crunching it with the shingle like an animal crunching bones.

The clay cliff ends abruptly at the village whose foundations are on tougher shale; but as we came in sight of the clustered cottages, we saw a heavy sea smash on to the ramparts of the old coastguard station, and its spray drive among the chimney pots like hail. Behind that rampart of masonry and cliff, however, the village with its street lamps already lighted, looked snug and secure, and soon we were moving down towards it, out of the sting of the wind.

'We'll drop these at the warehouse,' Marney said. 'Then you'd better come and have a cup of tea with us. I fancy Amy was going to bake some tarts this afternoon. God, I'm hungry!'

The thought of my own cottage, with the fire out, and my lunch things still on the table, and my pot-boiler not a word nearer completion, did not make a powerful counter inducement to this proposal. We left the cliff path where it drops by a rude stone stairway to the back end of the village, and took a short path, paved with mussel and limpet shells to a stone building which stood on a little ridge overlooking the sea, close by Henry Lunn's cottage. This was the warehouse. Pushing open the door, we were greeted by a cloud of tarry smoke through which was visible a hurricane lamp hanging from a rafter, and the flames of a fire burning in an open hearth at the far end of a barn-like room. Near the fireplace Henry Lunn was seated on a fish-box, the skeleton of a lobster pot leaning against his knee. We put down our faggots, and Marney closed the door.

'What the devil are you at?' he hailed his father. 'Have you started a smoked haddock factory? God — fit to suffocate you in here.'

Henry greeted us with a genial smile.

'I've been burning some old pot netting,' he explained quietly, 'and a great gust of wind blew down the chimney, just before you chaps came in. Where have you been all afternoon? Amy was up here asking after you a few minutes ago. You'd best get along sharp for your tea.'

Marney maintained a complete indifference to this piece of domestic news. I believed that he liked being fussed over by his wife; but he resented any suggestion that he was not master in his own home; free to come and go as he wished. We made our way through a clutter of boxes and barrels and coils of rope to the fireside, and Marney removed a fag-end from behind his ear and lit it nonchalantly with a smouldering stick.

'We've been up Browe Wood for hazels,' he said, 'and we've got a tidy lot, too, but we want a damned sight more if we're going to make a hundred pots this winter. What are you at? Are you still trying to make a shut-up pot?'

Henry grinned.

'No, I'm not,' he answered slowly. 'I know it can't be done. But I've mended two out of the three pots we saved from that last smash up, and I've nearly finished this one.'

He pushed the frame he had been working on to one side, took hold of another, completely netted, and put it across his knee. I must have seen thousands of such pots in my lifetime; but I realized, looking at this one closely, how vague my conception of a lobster pot had been: and I had still to learn what dearly-bought knowledge and cunning and craftmanship went into its construction; what an admirably efficient apparatus it was.

It consisted first of a rectangular base, made of wood slats, and measuring two feet by a foot and a half. The hazel hoops (which the Lunns called bows) were secured from side to side so as to form the skeleton of a miniature domed hut; and these were strengthened by a straight hazel along the top, and another at each side. The ends and roof were plainly netted with stout manilla twine; but the sides, divided by the middle bow, were so netted that one division could be opened, forming a door, and the other formed the entrance of a funnel (technically

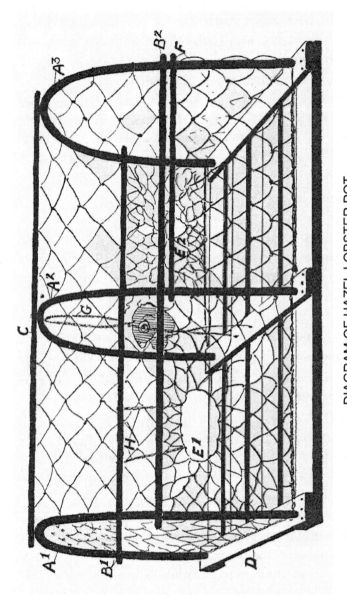

DIAGRAM OF HAZEL LOBSTER POT

A1-2-3 Bows; B1-2 Side Sticks; C Top Stick; D Bottom; E1-2 Spouts; F Door; G Bait String; H Spout Lashings 'spout'), a conical net reaching half way into the pot; an arrangement that was duplicated so that the two spouts entered diagonally opposite each other. I knew, of course, that the pots used by the Lunns differed from the Bramblewick pot (still used by the Fosdycks) for I remembered listening to arguments among the fishermen after the Sledburgh 'invasion', as to the respective merits of Bramblewick gear and that of the 'foreigners'. But even with the pot in front of me, I could not have told just then where the difference lay; and I did not feel inclined to confess to my ignorance by inquiring. I was interested, however; and Henry must have observed this, for he suddenly remarked:

'Aye, they're fine pots these of ours. I'd back them against any pot there is for catching lobsters, and for fishing in a strong tideway, and for general handiness. But they've got the same fault as all other pots. They take up too much room, particularly in a small boat like ours, when you're shifting ground, or when you want to take them out in a hurry from shallow water. That's how we lose them. You're fishing close in, and the weather turns bad sudden, and by the time you've got one coble load out to deep water, the rest are smashed up.'

'Aye,' put in Marney, with a faintly ironic smile, 'I was telling him about that while we were cutting hazels, and he asked me why we didn't have pot frames made of iron so that they wouldn't smash up at all. I told him iron wouldn't be any better than hazels in bad weather.'

Henry stared at his pot in silence for a while; then he remarked thoughtfully:

'I think that's daft to say that iron wouldn't be

stronger than wood. It stands to reason it would. But unless you had it galvanized it would soon rust and rot the netting away, and it would cost a lot of money. Pots are expensive enough as it is. I reckon that with the twine and the tows, and the time it takes to make one, a pot costs at least five shillings. No. There'd be no need to worry about them being smashed up, if you could make them shut up when you wanted. You could pack two hundred pots into a coble like ours at one go, and you'd hardly know you'd got them. But to be any use they'd have to be so that you could shut them up and open them again as quickly as you can open and shut an umbrella. And it can't be done. It can't be done.'

He fell into a thoughtful silence again. We all three continued to stare at the pot. I saw at once that Henry was right. It could not be done with a frame of hazels which owed what strength it possessed to the fact that its components were rigidily nailed together. But I perceived suddenly, and with a peculiar excitement, that if iron hoops were substituted for hazel hoops, they might be hinged, so that they could fall inwards, and lie flat on the pot bottom; and, because of their greater strength and rigidity, they would require only one straight bar to hold them erect, and that this bar might be used as a lever for performing the erecting and collapsing operation. I said nothing. With my excitement growing I measured visually the height of the two outer bows, and saw that when collapsed they would not foul each other. I saw at the same time that if this bar was divided, and one half used to couple one of the outer bows to the centre bow, these two might be regarded as one element, and the other half of the bar serve for the operating lever. All that would be required would be some means of locking this lever in the erect position, some sort of bolt or trigger that could be worked easily with one hand.

I was excited, but I did not think then of the possibilities of my discovery. I did not imagine then that I had invented something. My excitement was the childish one of having succeeded where a master had failed; and my immediate impulse was to show Henry and Marney how clever I was; but at that moment the door was opened and John Lunn came in.

He was washed and dressed, as he had been last night when he had called on me; but he looked even more spick and span and self-important.

'Hello,' he said, carefully avoiding the dirty barrels as he advanced towards us, 'are you helping father to make a shut-up pot?'

'Don't be so damned funny,' Marney retorted; and, with a half-envious glance at John's clothes, 'What are you dolled up for, are you going courting?'

John, while he affected at times a truculent misogynism, was undoubtedly envious of Marney's successful marriage; on the other hand Marney was not indifferent to the fact that bachelordom had certain advantages, freedom being the most important of them. John turned, with his back to the fire, and luxuriously lighted a new fag with a match.

'Amy was up here looking for you just now,' he said, grinning. 'Did father tell you?'

Marney ignored this, and John went on:

'I'm going to Burnharbour, since you're all so anxious to know. I'm going to see a chap who had a lot to do with getting up the Burnharbour Brass Band. I'm going to find out exactly how many instruments we'll want, and what they'll cost, and the best way to set about starting a band in Bramblewick.'

'You'd do better if you got your old clothes on again and started making at pot,' Henry remarked drily. 'You'll never get a brass band here if you live to be a hundred, or anything else that's new.'

John turned on his father hotly.

'Then what are you wasting your time for, trying to make a new sort of pot?'

'I'm doing it for myself, not for Bramblewick.'

'Well, I'm trying to start a band for myself as much as for anyone. It'll be worth it if only we can make enough row to drown the sound of that bloody sea on a winter's night. And anyway, I'm not asking you to join it. I came in to ask if you wanted me to fetch you anything back from Burnharbour.'

Henry smiled.

'There's nowt I want, unless you happen to go near that sweet shop on the pier. I'd like two pennorth of their acid drops. They're fresher than what you can buy in Bramblewick.'

'If Woolworth's is open, you can buy me a balloon,' said Marney ironically.

'Silent, or one that squeaks?' John countered as he made for the door.

We watched him go in silence; but as soon as the door was closed Marney said briskly:

'Corne on. We'd better be going for tea.'

I moved with him towards the door, but I took another look at the pot as I did so. My impulse to announce my discovery had gone before a stronger, more exciting plan to make a model and present it to the Lunns as an accomplished thing; and I surprised Marney when we got outside by telling him that I could not come to tea. We parted, and I hurried to my cottage.

5

On the opposite side of the street to my cottage, down a short flight of steps was a tiny sunless garden, and a building which originally had served the dual purpose of an extra kitchen and washhouse to the household proper. Except that it was laid with gas it had escaped the modernization of the rest of the property. The walls were limewashed stone, the floor was flagged, there was an old-fashioned kitchen hearth, and a window, overlooking the garden, which preserved its original panes of bottle glass. There was also a boiler, an enormous cement rain-water cistern, and an ancient gas-stove with an oven large enough to roast half a sheep, which luckily was not connected to the supply. The place had many shelves and cupboards (one of them a coal store), and there was a stout kitchen table near the window. It was here that I had done odd jobs like mending fishing rods, patching my sea boots, and sawing and chopping wood. I had a hammer, a Woolworth hack-saw, one or two files, a ruler, and a small fret-worker's vice. All that I needed, therefore, was material. I would make my experimental model two-thirds full size. I wanted wood to make a bottom, and some stout wire would serve for the bows instead of the stout iron rod I visualized for the practical design.

In one of the cupboards I found a soap-box full of clothes pegs. I emptied them and a nest of nibbled newspaper and a pregnant mouse on to the floor. The mouse escaped. I knocked the box to pieces, and set about making the pot bottom. But all the time I had been trying to remember where I had seen some suitable wire, and suddenly I remembered. The moon had not risen yet. I lighted a hurricane lamp and set off for the midden. Bramblewickers, ever since I could remember, had exercised a certain discretion in the disposal of their rubbish. The midden, with its sanitary self-closing doors, was for muck and ashes. But things like old bedsteads, pots and pans, broken oil stoves, were heaved into the bushes behind the midden. A discarded parrot cage, which I had observed some days ago was still there, and with this in one hand and my lamp in the other, I hurried back, with my mind too hot on my project to think what a peculiar sight I must have presented to Mrs. Brewster, who was just shaking the crumbs from her table-cloth as I passed her door.

I set the cage down, and continued with the making of the bottom. I worked in a fever heat, cursing the nails that bent and delayed me, and the wood that split. I was thirsty and hungry by the time I had done, and I had a sudden picture of Marney sitting down to his tea, and Amy's cakes hot from the oven, but I felt that I had no time even to go into the cottage for a drink of water. The bottom, except for its size, was merely a replica of a hazel pot bottom. I set to work on the parrot cage.

It was surprisingly well made. The wires I wanted were interlaced with finer ones, twisted and soldered. I had to bite these through with my pincers, and the ends left points like barbed wire, so that my fingers were bleeding before I had removed half a dozen clean pieces. These were too tough for the pincers. I tried the hack-saw, broke the blade, and finally had to cut them with a file.

I wanted three half hoops. Here again I found an unexpected problem; for while it is easy to bend a piece of wire double, it is extraordinarily difficult to make an even semi-circle of it. It gives in the wrong place, and having given, nothing less than hammering it completely straight again, will give you another fair chance of achieving the required shape. The whole job, I soon perceived, required coolness, and I could not be cool. I wanted to see my model finished. I wanted to see if the idea would work.

In the end I had to be content with three tolerably even bows. My next task was to make a short hook at the ends of each one, like the hooks in the handle of a pail. I discovered, however, that when I put one end in the vice and tried to bend it, the whole bow straightened out again and that I ought to have done this operation before I made the bow at all. I started afresh, with three new pieces of wire from the cage; and at last I had my bows complete; and they looked so much like the handles of a cheap pail or paint tin that I saw how I might have saved myself all this trouble if I had left my parrot cage alone, and searched the midden annexe for a couple of these utensils, which were plentiful enough. Yet I believed they would serve my present purpose; and already I had solved the problem as to how I should hinge them to the base. I went into the cottage, opened the closet where I had stored the redundant furniture, and hauled out three of the framed Conversation Pieces. It was a moment's work to cut their cords and unscrew the picture rings from their frames. Returning to the washhouse, I screwed these in at the ends and middle of the bottom, and, with unsteady fingers hooked the bows into them, holding them up, until the last one was secure. Then one by one I let them fall. They lay perfectly flat along the bottom, taking up scarcely a quarter of an inch more room than the bottom itself. So far so good.

I had still to make the coupling bar, joining the top of one of the outer bows to the top of the middle bow; and the erecting bar, looped to the other outer bow, and with its free end fastened to the middle bow when the contraption was erect: and I saw before I had finished them a new difficulty. To work as I had meant them to work, each of these bars would have to be hinged, dead in the centre of the bows. At present there was nothing to stop them sliding down and getting out of alignment. It seemed, however, as though I was gifted with a form of second sight, that I was inspired. As I slipped an end of the coupling bar on to the first bow, I saw that all I

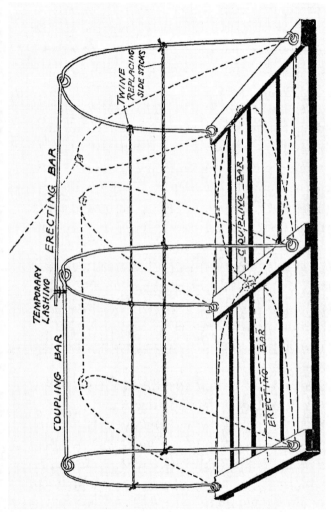

THE FIRST WIRE POT, UN-NETTED

Dotted lines show the frame partly collapsed and completely collapsed

wanted was a little kink in the top of the bow, in which the turned end of the bar would move, but only in the required direction. I detached the bows from the bottom. I made the kinks by holding the bows over the slightly open jaws of the vice, and hitting the wire with a chisel. The vice cracked, but did not break completely until the last one was finished.

My excitement now was very intense. My scratched and bleeding hands trembled as I attached the two coupled bows to the bottom. I left them in the collapsed position, while I put the erecting bar on the other bow and secured the bow to the bottom. Then, holding the free end of the erecting bar, I pushed up the bow to which it was attached. I lifted the middle bow, and its mate came up with it beautifully. The pot was erect, and all that it needed to retain it in that position was a piece of string, where the end of the erecting bar met the middle bow, and that piece of string could be superseded by a neat catch in the practical model. I let go of the bar. Of their own weight the bows fell down and lay neatly on the bottom.

It worked; as I had known from the first moment that it *must* work. I erected it again and tied it and placed it on the table. I lit a cigarette, and surveyed it, gloating. Nothing remained now but the net; and I was confident that the net could not possibly interfere with the folding process. Should I show it to Henry Lunn first, or to Marney? I thought that if I went round to Marney, it was possible that the tea things were still on the table. I collapsed the pot again, wrapping it up in a newspaper and hurried out. I was surprised at once to find a complete change in the weather. The wind had dropped. The moon had risen and shone brightly in a clear and frosty sky. My next surprise was to find that the shops were closed. I heard a clock strike eight, as I reached Marney's cottage.

There was no sign of tea things as I stepped inside. The table was littered with bundles and strands of brightly coloured wool, and Marney and his wife were sitting in front of the fire weaving the wool into a piece of fabric, one portion of which presented the appearance of a patterned rug, with a diamond of emerald green growing inside a striped border of black and yellow and red. Amy smiled. Marney moved his chair back and signed to me to take another; and then invited me to inspect their combined handiwork, which he spread across his knee, so that none of its splendour should be lost.

'We've done all this since tea-time,' he said proudly. 'It's bonny, isn't it? I reckon it's champion the way that green shows against those other colours.'

I put my parcel on the table, waiting a more dramatic moment for its disclosure. I observed Marney's bouquet on the mantelpiece, stuck in a bright blue and gilt vase. I told him that the rug when finished would look fine in front of the fire.

'Eh! We're not going to put it there, to get messed up!' cried Amy. 'It's going to be for the bedroom.'

'Aye,' Marney agreed. 'And, besides, we may win a prize with it. The firm that sells you the wool and this patent stuff to fix it in, offers a prize of thirty bob for the best rug sent in every month. You see the stuff's got a pattern marked on it. You can get different patterns of course. Some have diamonds in the middle, like this. Others have squares or circles. But you have to use your own judgement as to how to mix your colours. And the best one wins the prize. . . . But I reckon these sort of rugs are for women and kids to make,' he added, suddenly reaching his hand under his chair, and producing a genuine sailor's mat made of unlaid rope drawn through the fabric of tough sailcloth. 'These are the sort I like. Only I'll admit they're not so bonny, being all the same colour and having no pattern. Anyway, it's something to pass the time with, when there's nowt else to do.'

'Why didn't you come and have your tea?' asked Amy. 'Marney said you might come on later, and we kept it on the table until six o'clock.'

'Did you have any tea?' said Marney. 'We can easily make you a cup now, if you like, and there's plenty of cakes left.'

I had the courage to refuse; and I took hold of my parcel. But I suddenly felt extremely nervous, afraid of Marney's irony. I felt that I was going to make a fool of myself with this attempt of mine to improve on an apparatus which, despite its faults, had served so many generations of fishers. And Marney's first remark when I opened the parcel did not encourage me.

'What the hell have you got there? Have you been making a mouse trap?'

I swore, in order to give myself confidence.

'No. It's a bloody lobster pot. Only one that shuts up. It's only a model, of course.'

Marney stood up, and looked at it, with an expression

on his face which I took to be one of contemptuous scorn. And I found no encouragement in his next remark.

'A lobster pot? That thing's not meant to be a pot frame, is it?'

I was aware that the drama of my disclosure was falling painfully flat.

'It isn't one like yours, of course,' I said. 'It's a collapsing pot, and, of course, it's only two-thirds proper size. You're all saying that a shut-up pot would be useful. Well, this is an experimental model, just to see if it can be done.'

'Then how does the damned thing work?'

I stood up, feeling very much like a nervous speaker rising to address an unsympathetic audience. I took hold of the end of the erecting bar and awkwardly jerked the first bow upright. Then, after a great deal of fumbling, I managed to get the other two upright, and the erecting bar into its correct position. This was to have been my moment of triumph; but on Marney's face I saw nothing but an ironic grin.

'Garn,' he said. 'That's no use. A thing like that would be no use to a fisherman. It shuts up and opens all right, but it isn't a pot frame at all. It hasn't got any side sticks. Where do you think you're going to fasten your netting. Have you forgotten the net? Let it go down again.'

I did so; and I thought for a moment that Marney was impressed; for it collapsed infinitely better than it had opened.

'It certainly shuts up,' he said. 'Open it again.'

I opened it, a trifle more skilfully this time, and tied it, explaining as I did so my idea for a locking catch.

Marney was no longer grinning; but beyond this there was nothing in his face to suggest genuine approval.

'Aye,' he said. 'It's all right. It's clever. But I don't think it's any use. Iron's no use, I tell you. It would rust, and anyway it would cost too much. Besides, I don't see how it could be netted, not to make it like one of ours. And I don't think it would shut up like that if it was netted, either; I'm damned certain it wouldn't. What do you think about it, Amy?'

Amy was preparing to get on with the mat again.

'You needn't ask me,' she answered. 'If I said anything, you'd only say I knew nowt about it. If you and your father say you want a shut-up lobster pot, you ought to help someone who's trying to help you, and not discourage them by saying it's no good before you've tried it. You're like that, you are! You said these rugs would be no good until you saw me start one; and now, to hear you talk, it might have been you who thought of it first; aye, even before the folks who invented it. . . . Before you say it won't work properly with a net, you ought to try and put a net on, and not just condemn it.'

It was an unexpected championing; and Amy followed up subtly:

'If *you* can't put a net on it, I should think your father could, easily enough.'

'I didn't say I couldn't,' Marney answered quickly, looking at the pot with a new interest. 'Anyone could put some sort of a net on it, if they studied it out. But it would have to go on different to ours. You'd want a bit of twine stretching across instead of our side sticks. It wouldn't work so well, I know.'

He took a piece of twine from his pocket, and tied a length of it along one side. I said nothing. He cut it and tied another length along the other side. Then he stood back, looking at the whole thing earnestly.

'I don't like the looks of it,' he said. 'That twine will sag when you net on to it. It will spoil the look of the whole thing. You wouldn't have to use ordinary thick twine either with it being so small. It wants fishing line. I had a ball of fishing line the other day, Amy; do you know what happened to it? And I had a small netting needle for making an onion bag.'

Amy got up.

'You do need a lot of looking after,' she said, going to a cupboard. 'If only you'd put things away when you'd done with them, you might know where to find them.'

She produced a ball of line and a needle. While she had been searching, Marney had stared at the pot in silence. I pushed my tin of fags in front of him. He took no notice of it and began to fill the needle, still staring at the pot. I did not speak. Whether Marney had changed his opinion about the thing or not, I knew that he had become deeply interested in it. When the needle was full, he took hold of the pot, and put it on his knees, end up.

After a moment's consideration, he knotted an end of the line, low down on the leg of one of the outer bows, stretched it to the other leg, then along to the other bows and back to his starting point, so that he had a continuous line along the whole pot bottom. He cut this off from the needle, and stopped again to consider. Then he put a clove-hitch on to the first section of the line he had made, dipped the needle over the line again, and with another clove-hitch formed a half mesh. Quick as an old woman knitting, he made a series of half meshes along the whole section of line, passed the needle round the leg of the bow, and began to work back, forming now from each half mesh a recognizable diamond.

I was fascinated. I forgot for the time being that he was making the net on my own pot. He worked so quickly that I could not follow the course taken by his needle in forming the netting knot. The netting grew from his fingers as though by conjury. He reached the other leg, and without pausing, worked forward again, forming another row. In less than five minutes the whole of one end of the pot was netted and then, for the first time, he paused.

'It's not going to look right,' he said. 'It's having no side sticks that's going to spoil it.'

He pointed his needle at the first pieces of twine he had tied on in place of the rigid side stays of the hazel pot.

'I've got to go along the whole top now, netting from side to side, and that twine is simply bound to sag. If you show this to father when it's done, it'll be the first thing he'll go for. He's a hard chap to please is our old man. I don't want to have him laughing at me if it looks a mess.'

'You've made a lovely job of that end, anyway,' said Amy subtly; looking up from her own task. 'You might have measured those meshes with a ruler.'

In my examination of Henry Lunn's pot, I had thought of the two side sticks only as giving strength and stiffness to the frame, and had not reckoned on them as giving independent support to the net. I could see now that being replaced with string, the net would sag. But I said nothing, hoping that this would not make any vital difference to the whole apparatus. Marney went on netting along the 'roof'. The sag developed, but he did not remark on it, until he covered in the roof, netted the other end, and cut off. Then he put the pot on the table and eyed it critically.

'It doesn't look so bad after all,' he muttered. 'It doesn't look so bad. I like those small meshes. I reckon they look champion. . . . But I still think it's going to be no use,' he added. 'It's not going to shut up and open again like it did, now it's netted. Shall we try it now, or shall we wait till I've put the doors and the spouts in?'

It was my first indication since he had started, that Marney was thinking about the collapsing properties of the pot; and I imagined that I saw just a suspicion of my own excitement and anxiety in his eyes when I told him that I preferred him to finish it, so that the test would be final.

'All right,' he said. 'Only don't say it's my fault if it doesn't work. You can't put a man's shirt on a bairn remember, and expect it to be a fit. I'll net one of our pots with my eyes closed. But this is different. Aye, almost every knot comes different.'

He started to fill his needle again.

Amy suddenly got up.

'Good Lord!' she cried. 'It's nearly nine o'clock, and I haven't started to get supper ready yet. I'll want that table in a minute, and don't sprawl yourselves over the fire and get in my way.'

We moved out of the way.

'Set the table for three,' said Marney. 'There's still

plenty of that ling left, and I'll swear he had no tea. I'll make the spouts first, and leave the doors till after.'

Putting the pot on his knee again, he swiftly put a row of half meshes round one of the four square spaces remaining between the legs of the bows and the netted roof. Then he began making a spout. Once more I forgot my personal interest in the pot, so fascinated was I by his hands, and the net they wove. This did not close in upon the space. It grew outwards in rows which by some trick that I could not comprehend, formed a gradually narrowing open cone. And when it was projecting about two inches from the pot, Marney, by further trickery, finished it off so that its orifice was bound, as it were, with an even circle of line. He at once pushed it into the pot, turning it inside out, and he stretched and tied it to the opposite side so that it became in effect a funnel, reaching in to the pot's middle. He paused again, and looked at it critically.

'I've made many a worse spout than that!' he said. 'If I can make another as good, I'll not mind if father does see it. I bet he can't make a better!'

He turned the pot round and started the second spout, in the diagonally opposite space.

'You know the spouts are the most important thing in a pot. They're everything. The bait goes fair in the middle of the pot of course, and you've got to have your spouts run as near to it as you can, without being so near that a lobster can shove his claw through a mesh, and nip off a bit before he gets in. Lobsters aren't like crabs, you know. They're not greedy. I think they feed mostly on sea-weed, and they only like a bit of fish now and again, just like

78

some folks fancy a sausage for breakfast, instead of bacon. If they get a snip they'll not bother to go inside at all. They'll just swim away until they find a nice quiet spot to eat it: so you make the spouts just clear the bait, and 'tice them right inside.'

During this time I was aware vaguely of the clatter of crockery; the splutter of boiling fat; and then, less vaguely, of the smell of frying fish. But we were both startled when Amy cried briskly:

'Come on, you can leave that now. Supper's ready.'

Marney had finished the second spout.

'I'll just tie it up, Amy,' he said. 'It won't take a minute.'

'I know your minutes. Put it down, and finish it after. You're like a bairn with a toy.'

But Marney had already pushed the spout inside, stretched it, and now he quickly tied it. It was the exact twin of the first one.

'It's a beauty!' he cried, holding up the whole pot between his two hands, and turning it about. 'I've never made a better pair of spouts in my life. We might try and shut it up now. The doors won't make that much difference.'

Amy suddenly stepped across and snatched it from his hands, and put it under the table.

'For God's sake come and get your supper before everything's cold. And you can shut up about lobster pots until we've finished. You pour out the tea, while I serve the fish.'

We started supper, and I did not realize until then how hungry I was. But our conversation, with the subject of lobster pots banned, was constrained. Marney, usually most talkative at meal times, scarcely spoke at all. He remarked that the wind had dropped nicely, but that there wasn't much chance of getting to sea to-morrow, unless there came a blow from the land. And he also remarked soon that he hadn't much appetite, that he didn't want any more fish, and that he'd finish up with only a tart. Even my own hunger was quickly satisfied.

'We'll give you a hand with clearing the table,' said Marney at last. 'We can finish our tea by the fireside:

'You needn't trouble,' said Amy drily. 'You don't usually. You'd better get that thing finished before it's bedtime.'

Marney picked up the pot and his needle.

'You know,' he remarked, 'I've been thinking all the time we've been having supper that it's no good having our sort of doors on this pot. Ours have a stick in them, and they let down. But if you have a stick, it's bound to get in the way when it shuts up, even if nothing else does. All we want here are two pieces of straight netting, only leaving one edge of them free. They'll slide up and down the bows and to fasten them you'll just lace them to the bottom twine.'

This was much too complicated for my theoretical comprehension; but as soon as he had netted one of the two remaining spaces, I understood. For what he had made was really a curtain, looped on to the bows, which could be raised and lowered with a movement of the hand, and securely closed with a short length of line. I expressed my admiration but Marney said nothing. He turned the pot round, and made a similar door in the last space. This done, he opened one of the doors and tied a double piece of line from the top to the bottom of the pot, dead in the centre, and put a sliding loop on it. Then he took some of the coloured rug-wool, jammed this with the loop, to represent a bait, closed the door, and put the pot on the table. It was finished.

We looked at it in dead silence. Amy had cleared the table, and was back in her chair. Marney stood with his back to the fire, without taking his eyes from the pot. He lit a fag.

'Well,' he said at last, and in a voice that was perceptibly unsteady, 'I don't like to boast, but I reckon that's the bonniest little lobster pot I've ever seen. It looks champion. Look at those spouts! Damned if you could tell one from the other. The only fault I have to find with it is that twine where it sags, where the side sticks ought to be. If it was only a bit smaller, and made with hazels, I'd have it on the mantelpiece for an ornament.' He paused: and added with a sudden tenseness: 'Well, let's see if the damned thing will work. Let's see if it *will* shut up, and open again.'

I knew at once that all this boasting was bluff, that he was just as excited as I was myself. I stood up and drew the pot towards me. I untied the knot, and took hold of the free end of the erecting bar, and gave it a slight pull. And with that the three bows fell, taking the net with them, and lay flat upon the bottom, with the folded net taking up not more than a fraction of an inch more room than the naked frame did previously.

'Put it up again!' Marney shouted.

The erecting bar had come outside the net, and lay ready to hand. I pulled it, and gave the centre bow an upward jerk. The pot became erect and rigid. I let it go. It collapsed. Marney strode over to the table. He erected it again and collapsed it. Then he pushed it across to Amy.

'You have a go at it,' he cried excitedly. 'You have a go at it.'

Amy worked it without the slightest difficulty. She giggled.

'It's like a Jack-in-the-box!'

'It's champion! It's champion!' Marney cried, taking it again. 'Damn it — it's the cleverest thing I've ever seen. It beats everything. God, if we had three fleets of pots like that, only full size, we could stow them in the coble and never know they were there. You could take them out in winter time, and let them fish while you were hauling your lines... That is, of course, if they'd fish like ours.'

He suddenly became horribly contemplative again.

'Aye, if they'd fish as well as our's,' he repeated slowly. 'I can't see why this sort of pot shouldn't, but there's no doubt it's different, and as I've said before lobsters are very queer things. It's a pity we'll not be able to go to sea to-morrow, or we might drop it just outside the Landing on the way out, and give it a trial.'

'I tell you what,' he added, quite excited again, 'there's plenty of deep holes round the scaur ends, and it will be a very low tide to-night. Why shouldn't we bait it with a bit of that ling, and go down and set it, and get it at low tide to-morrow? That would be better than showing it to father now, and anyway he'll be in bed. It's big enough to catch a small lobster. God — it would be a surprise for father and John, if we took it to them with a lobster in it, and then showed them how it shut up.'

I agreed; but before I had time to say so, Amy cut in, indignantly:

'You'll do nothing of the sort. It's past bed-time now, and I'm not going to sit up for you while you go prowling about the scaurs. He can easily set it himself if he wants to. You'll not prove anything until you see it to-morrow.'

'Garn!' said Marney, with a gleam of truculence, 'it won't take more than a minute or two, and I've got to go out anyway to see what the weather's doing.'

A slight domestic tension had developed, but I was too excited to worry as to whether Amy was really cross. Marney moved quickly to the pantry and returned with a piece of raw fish which he secured in the pot in place of the wool. He then produced from a cupboard some thin rope, a cork, and a flat piece of iron.

'I'd forgotten the ballast,' he said. 'I'll lash this piece of iron in. It won't take up much room.'

He did so, and then collapsed the pot. He paused again to admire the effect. Even with the bait and ballast, it was no more bulky than a folded shirt.

'We'll leave it shut up,' he said. 'And we'd better wrap the paper round it again. There may be someone on the Slipway, and there's no point in letting all Bramblewick know about it.'

'We won't be more than ten minutes,' he said to Amy, as we moved to the door.

Amy had resumed work on the rug.

'I don't care if you're all night,' she said tartly, without looking up.

To this Marney said nothing, but as soon as we got outside, he remarked, uneasily:

'I don't think I'll come right down with you. I'll just come to the Slipway foot, and see if the swell's falling at all.'

The sky was still clear and frosty, and there was no wind, but the noise of the sea seemed as strong as ever, and I felt less eager for the experiment when we reached the Slipway and saw the lines of moonlit surf breaking on the dark scaur ends. Two men were walking up the Slipway from the shore.

'It's the Fosdycks,' Marney growled. 'Keep that thing hidden. We don't want them to see it.'

It was Luke and Tindal Fosdyck, the only two members of the old 'fishermen Fosdycks' who were still whole-time fishers (although a young sailor nephew, Tom Fosdyck, was fishing with them this winter). They were big men, and despite that they were both well past middle age, powerful. They were gruff in their manner, humourless, secretive, and unfriendly. As a boy I had hated them, for unlike the Sledburgh 'foreigners', they would never let you set foot in their boats, or let you watch them baiting their lines, or mending nets; and I remembered how Luke and Tindal had on one occasion stood by approvingly while a gang of patriots had hided me with 'tangles', and then ducked me in a rock pool where the Fosdycks had been gutting their fish.

And even now, while I could admire them objectively as men, admire their courage, their seasoned strength, even their stubborn conservatism, I could sense the old enmity, the unyielding hatred of the 'foreigner', in the very way they looked at you when they spoke, with a humourless smile, and a hard twinkle in their eyes, which at its kindest seemed to convey a contemptuous pity. And I was aware that Marney was bristling like a dog, although he gave a polite enough rejoinder to Luke's 'Now then' as we passed.

'Now Luke,' he said. 'Wind's dropped.'

'Aye,' Luke answered over his shoulder. 'But there still a lot of sea.'

We stopped at the bottom of the Slipway. Marney glanced up to the Dock before he spoke, and he kept his voice low.

'We don't want *them* to know about this. If I were you I wouldn't tell a soul about it, except father and John. I tell you, I think it's a champion idea. If only they'll fish as well as our pots, and you can make them cheap, I reckon you could make tons of brass out of shut-up pots.'

He handed me the line and cork.

'God, I wish I could come down with you,' he added, regretfully, 'but I don't like to leave Amy and the bairn by themselves late at night like this. If I were you I'd set it down the Landing. It will be safe there if you put a big stone on the rope; and it's a good spot for a lobster. I'll go with you for it in the morning. I'll call for you about eleven, if you're not down first; and I'll bring a sack, in case there's anyone 'bout.'

I asked him to say good night for me to Amy, and thank her for my supper. Then we parted, and I hurried down to the sea, with my patent lobster pot under my arm, and a great excitement inside me.

6

I was awakened next morning by Marney shouting up my stairs:

'Ahoy! Are you there?'

I made an answering noise.

'Eh!' he shouted. 'Have you forgotten about that patent pot of your's? It's gone eleven o'clock. You'll have to look sharp if you're going to get it before the tide flows. If you'll tell me where you shot it, I'll go and get it if you like.'

I got out of bed, and into my clothes, as though he had told me the house was on fire, and hurried down stairs.

'You've got the room in a hell of a mess again,' was Marney's greeting. 'You ought to let Amy come in and clear things up for you.'

I did not see the room; not Marney, for that matter; only my sea-boots; and as soon as I had got them on, and lit a fag, I told Marney that I was ready.

'Where did you set it?' he inquired, as we hurried down the Dock.

I had put it in the Landing, just over the scaur edge, where, the night before last, I had made such a peculiar catch.

'God, I wouldn't have put it there,' Marney commented. 'Not in the very same spot. I reckon that's asking for bad luck. By the way, I haven't told father or John anything about it. They're up in the warehouse, baiting. If there's anything in it, we'll take it up as it is, and surprise them. I'm dying to see our old man's face.'

We had reached the Slipway Top. By this time I had sufficiently recovered from the shock of my awakening to observe that the wind was off the land, the air mild, and that nothing but a heavy ground-swell remained of yesterday's rough sea. The tide was very low. But we could not see the Landing until we had passed the end of the breakwater. And when we did so it was with mutual dismay, for two men were on the scaur, close to where the pot was set. Marney swore.

'It' s Luke and Tindal getting flithers [1]! I'll be damned! It's the first time I've seen them flithering on the Landing Scaur this year. With all the Bay to choose from, it's a queer thing that they should decide to go there this morning. Well, we can't go and haul it under their noses. We'd better mess about a bit.'

We walked slowly down the Landing.

'I wonder how long they're going to be,' Marney went on testily. 'The tide's flowing. Whereabouts exactly is it set?'

I observed with growing dismay that Luke Fosdyck was now bending down snicking 'flithers' off the scaur, not more than a few feet from where, in the water, the cork of the pot should have been visible; and that he was slowly decreasing that distance.

'It will be a wonder if he doesn't see it,' Marney said. 'He's got eyes like a hawk, has old Luke, particularly for

[1] Limpets

anything you don't want him to see. How the hell can we get them out of the way before the tide flows. For two pins I'd go and fire off the lifeboat gun. Look, he's standing up now, shouting to Tindal, and looking over the scaur. He must have seen it.'

It was a tense moment. Luke was standing erect, gazing it seemed to me, at the very place where the cork should be floating, and Tindal had joined him. They seemed to be talking. But suddenly Luke picked up his basket; and the pair of them began to walk leisurely up the scaur.

We watched them with assumed indifference, moving ourselves down the east scaur, so that we should not pass them. The tide was flowing fast, and the swell was breaking right across the Landing mouth. The tangle of oar-weed which at dead low of a spring tide breaks the surface beyond the scaur ends, was already hidden; but it was almost as though the Fosdycks knew of our anxiety, so slowly did they move, so often did Luke stop to light his pipe.

'Damn it, you'd think they'd both got bunions on their feet,' grumbled Marney.

Not until they had crossed the dry part of the Landing under the village cliff did we venture to cross it in the opposite direction, and close down to the tide's edge, and even then we endeavoured to convey, by stopping occasionally and poking among the weed and sand, that we were merely foraging for bits of coal and jet.

'I bet they saw that cork,' Marney muttered. 'But they must have decided it was a cod-line some lad had set. I wonder if they're going to stop on the Slipway?'

We watched them walk slowly up the Slipway. For a moment it seemed that they were going to stop near the coast-guard wall, a favourite gossiping place for the male villager; but to our relief they moved on and out of sight. We at once walked swiftly down the west scaur over which the spent 'runs' of the outside breakers were already washing. Just beyond the marking post my cork was visible.

'I don't think there'll be a lobster in it,' Marney remarked with an unsuccessful nonchalance, as we reached it, 'the water's too mucky. Besides, it's a new pot, and even our pots won't fish when they're new. I reckon it will be empty. You haul it, and we'll pop it straight into the sack.'

We were wading almost knee-deep. The cork, however, was near enough for me to reach. I hauled on the stone first. Before I had got hold of the actual pot line the 'run' from a big sea came in and filled Marney's deck boots.

'Hurry up, for God's sake,' he shouted. 'The next sea will be up to our waists.'

I hauled, and the pot broke the surface. Marney grasped it and we rushed back to the dry part of the scaur, Marney leading, and it was not until he stopped and turned, with a triumphant shout, and held the pot out to me that I saw that it contained two lobsters.

Yesterday, had I seen a pot hauled, and half a dozen fine lobsters in it, it would have interested me no more than the sight of a dead rat in a trap. Now, the sight of two small lobsters, an inch at least under the legal size, filled me with a wild exultation; and Marney behaved as though he had never caught a lobster before.

'I wouldn't have thought it possible!' he shouted. 'I knew they were good spouts, those, but late in the season like this, and with the water mucky, God, it shows the damned thing will fish. If it had been a full-sized pot I bet it would have had a full-sized lobster in it, too. We're not going to put these back in the sea because they're undersize. No one's going to see them now that the Fosdycks are out of the way. Come on, we'll put it in the sack, just as it is, and go and show it to father.'

We put it in the sack, and Marney slung the sack over his shoulder. We rewarded ourselves with fags, lighting them ritually, like a savage might light a triumphant fire alongside a kill. We hurried up the Landing. But before we had reached the Slipway Foot, Marney remarked almost in a whisper,

'We'll not chance going up the Dock. We want to keep this job dark. It's likely as not the Fosdycks haven't gone home yet.'

We cut across the edge of the scaur, walked under the old coast-guard station, and made our way up the greasy, tumbling clay cliff, to the warehouse. We stepped in, Marney leading, and I closed the door behind me. Henry and John were just finishing the baiting of their lines. Neither as much as glanced up, but Henry muttered:

'Now then.' To which Marney said nothing.

At once some of my elation vanished, and Marney himself exhibited signs of nervousness, as he put the sack down on a barrel, strode over to the cold fireplace, and lit another fag. Then as though to disassociate himself from the business, he remarked quietly:

'*You'd* better show them what we've got.'

At that, both Henry and John turned round, and Henry observed the sack.

'What have you got there?' he said.

John too had seen the sack.

'I know what it is. They've been on to Garry Beck poaching. I saw a salmon there myself the other day. But they're no good this time of year. They're not worth eating. They're not worth the risk of being summoned and fined for. I don't see what there is to make such a mystery about.'

This seemed to give Marney confidence.

'Maybe you don't,' he said. 'And maybe it isn't a salmon at all,' and to me he added, 'Go on. Take it out.'

I opened the sack, and feeling very much as I did when I first disclosed the frame to Marney, took the pot out. And again there was a deadly silence. But it was broken effectively by the clatter of the lobster's tails on the pot bottom; a noise which, I was to learn in time, was one of the most pleasant a lobster fisherman could hear. Henry left go of his line. He turned and stared.

'What is it?' he said. 'Have you put those ninycocks [1] in it? Or has it caught them? What's the idea?'

'They're only ninycocks, they're both undersize,' said John, also leaving his task.

Marney stepped forward, grinning, and struck the attitude of a showman.

'We know they're undersize,' he said. 'But they're

[1] Ninycock = undersize lobster.

lobsters, aren't they? They've got eight legs apiece, and two claws. And this is a patent pot, made small for experimenting with. And there's the inventor of it,'—he pointed a hand in my direction—'although I put the net on it. And you needn't say owt about it until you see how it works. It's been set in the Landing all night. We only brought it up to you like this to show you it can fish. We'll take the lobsters out first. . . This,' he added with a touch of personal pride, 'is a patent door.'

He pulled the slip-knot of the short line which held one of the doors, smartly collared the lobsters, and put them on a barrel, then fastened the door again.

'If that's your patent,' Henry remarked, 'I don't think much of it. Our doors are twice as easy to work as that. It all looks daft to me.'

'*And* to me,' said John. 'What's the idea?'

'Show them,' said Marney laconically.

I undid the knot. A touch on one bow, and the pot collapsed.

'Now do you think it all looks daft!' said Marney, triumphantly.

There was a silence; a silence more complete and lasting than before. I looked at John. His face wore an expression of blank surprise. I looked at Henry. There was surprise in his face too, but there was something more than that. There was a look of profound interest.

'Will it go up again?' he said at last, and very quietly.

To my relief, Marney took on the responsibility of further demonstration. He erected the pot, and explained more effectively than I could have done myself, my idea for a lock, instead of a string.

'Try it yourself,' he said.

Henry did so.

John moved near.

'Let me have a go,' he demanded.

He too, collapsed and erected it. But Henry promptly took it from him, and repeated the operation. Again there was a silence, more tense than ever; for Henry's face had become mask-like; and we all three watched him as a court might watch a judge about to pronounce sentence. But I did not guess how that verdict was to affect me. Until now my interest in the pot had been little more than that of a boy making an ingenious model 'out of his own head' and astonishing his elders with it. I had got my fun out of it, and it would not have broken my heart if Henry had suddenly grinned and gone on baiting his line. I would have known at least that his judgement had been sound, pronounced from that deep knowledge which his life of conflict with the sea had given him. To Marney's judgment on such an issue I would not have attached great weight. In him the dramatic instinct was too strong. While fundamentally sincere he would exaggerate and flatter in order to impress. As for John, like most dogmatic people, he suffered from an inner indecisiveness, and in most matters pertaining to his craft at least, he merely followed his father's lead.

We waited while father looked at the pot, and we looked at father. And then father, who himself was not wanting in the dramatic instinct said very slowly, very quietly, and without taking his eyes from the pot:

'Well, do you want to know what I think of it?'

'Aye,' said Marney in a subdued voice. 'But remember

it's only a model.'

'Well, I'll tell you,' Henry answered, very slowly, very quietly: then, very deliberately he said, 'It's *champion!*'

My heart leapt. I had a sudden foolish desire to shake his hand, to shake everybody's hand; such had been the court-like tension of the last minute: so judicially dramatic was that pronouncement. Marney's face was beaming with delight. John's face, too, wore an approving grin. But Henry, having delivered his verdict, did not stop at that.

'I'll tell you what,' he went on, still deliberately. 'I'll tell you what. If you could make a full-sized pot that would shut up and open as well as that, with its bows and other parts of the frame galvanized, and so that it won't cost very much more than a hazel pot, you'd be putting hundreds of pounds into the pockets of the inshore fisherman. Now just take my case alone. I've been fishing off and on for lobsters for a good thirty years. Every year I've made at least a hundred pots. A pot such as ours with the labour that goes into it is worth at least five bob; call it twenty-five pounds for the hundred anyway, and call it twenty-five pounds dead loss every year, for if you don't lose them they wear out. Twenty-five pounds a year for thirty years is . . .'   .

'Seven hundred and fifty pounds,' I said.

'God, it's a lot of brass,' said Marney. 'And that doesn't include tows, and buoys and anchors that go when you have a smash up.'

'Just swallowed up by the sea,' said John, 'as I was telling him the other night. And there's fishermen who have lost over three hundred pots in a season!'

'We lost a hundred and fifty this year,' Henry continued. 'At Burnharbour in that first gale I should think at least a thousand pots were lost in one go.'

'And it's not only along this coast,' said Marney, 'it's the same everywhere they fish for lobsters.'

'Aye,' put in John again. 'Reckon up in cash what's lost in this country, and Scotland and Ireland, and Norway, and France, and Canada, and the States— why—as I was telling him the other night, it would run into thousands of pounds, into hundreds of thousands. Reckon what's lost in say ten years, and—damn it—it would be millions.'

'And they're nearly all lost for the same reason,' Henry went on. 'Because of them being such awkward things to stow. And remember it's not just the value of your gear that's lost. When there's a smash up it stops you fishing, and you've got to spend days of good fishing weather ashore making new ones. . . . I tell you, that if we had shut-up pots we wouldn't lose one of them in a season. They'd save us pounds, and they'd make us pounds!'

I was drinking giddy wine: and there was still more to drink: for Henry holding up the pot looked at it, and said with grave excitement:

'And that's not the only way shut-up pots would make brass. At present there's practically no lobstering done except in spring and summer, and a bit in autumn. Why? Because in cold weather lobsters go out to deep water, miles from shore. I bet you wouldn't have caught those two in another fortnight. But I know of rocky grounds twenty miles from shore where there's any amount of lobsters in midwinter. Big 'uns too. Bigger than you'll ever get close in. It wouldn't be safe to take pots like ours so far in winter time. You might want a bigger boat of course, and work out of Burnharbour, but in a big motor coble, you could take two hundred shut-up pots easily. And think of the price you'd get for lobsters in midwinter.'

'You'd make more brass in one week than you'd make in a whole winter of cod fishing,' said Marney fervently. 'You could fish for lobsters the whole year round.'

'I reckon you've got a fortune in that invention,' John pronounced solemnly. 'A fortune. You ought to patent it. If you can make it cheap enough, you'd sell thousands, all over the world. Hundreds of thousands. Think of the chap who first made a hairpin with a kink in it! He became a millionaire. Think of Edison and Marconi!'

'Aye,' put in Henry, more soberly. 'But the main thing is that it will give the inshore fisherman a chance to make a living again. Have you shown it to anyone else?'

'The Fosdycks were having a good look at the buoy when we went down to it,' Marney answered. 'But they didn't haul it, and the water was too mucky for them to see it without. There's only Amy.'

'Then if I were you,' Henry went on, looking to me, 'I wouldn't show it to anybody. *We'll* say nowt about it. Keep it dark. There's not a worse place anywhere for things getting talked about than Bramblewick. The main thing is to get a full size one made, and see if it works as well. Then work out what it's going to cost. If I were you I'd go up to the Thorpe blacksmith, and get the bows made proper. You needn't show him the whole thing. I'd doubt if he'd know it was a lobster pot anyway. But you could find out what iron costs, and how much more it costs to get it galvanized. Put this one in the sack again if you're going to carry it home. . . I'll tell you again—it's a champion idea. Champion! Only you don't want to waste any time getting that big one made. Bring it to me when you've got it made. I'll net it for you!'

'You needn't trouble,' Marney said quickly, as he hid the pot in the sack again. '*I'll* net it. What about these two ninycocks? Shall I get Amy to boil them for you? Or shall I put them in the sack?'

I asked him to put them in the sack: for I was thinking exultantly of the millions of lobsters my pots would catch; the dizzy fortune they were to make for me; and I felt that I could afford to be generous to its first two youthful victims and put them back in the sea to grow. But I doubted Marney's willingness to co-operate in such a sacrifice and I carried the sack myself as we moved quickly to the door.

7

I was hungry, but I refused Marney's invitation to go back and have a bit of dinner, and show the pot and its catch to Amy. I wished to be alone, to think, to get things into perspective. I hurried down the cliff path, thence by the back of the gas-works, and up to the Green and the midden route to my cottage. As I turned round the corner of the Brewster's cottage, however, I found myself face to face with Reub Brewster himself, in his sea-boots, and with a basket of bait in his hand. Evidently he had just come up from the shore. I admired Reub, as I admired the Fosdycks. He had, despite his shore profession, all the qualities of the seafaring Bramblewicker: and in the salmon season I had known him put out in his small rowing boat in stormy weather when even the Lunns and the Fosdycks had been doubtful whether to fish or haul up their cobles to the Dock. But he had, save on the rare occasions when he was tipsy, the true Bramblewick dourness, the same way of looking at a 'foreigner' when he spoke, with a humourless smile and something in his eyes suggestive of a secret mockery. Usually we had little to say to each other beyond the customary 'Now then.' I was startled when he put his basket down on his cottage door step, and turned as though to intercept me.

'Now then,' he said. 'Did you get owt this morning?'

I clutched guiltily at the sack, thinking that either the pot or the undersized lobsters must be showing. But to my relief he added:

'You had a line set down by the Landing posts, hadn't you? I saw you and Marney Lunn taking it up after the tide had begun to flow.'

I took my clue and lied, saying we had got two small ones. I imagined that he gave the sack a suspicious glance but all he said was:

'Aye. I thought it must be a line. I was going to set one there myself this morning but I saw a cork, so I went on to Black Scaur and set it there instead. There ought to be a few cod about with all this swell on. Did you take your's up?'

'Aye,' I said, edging past him.

'Then maybe I'll change mine over there to-night if I don't get owt. It's a good spot is the Landing.'

I stepped into my cottage, closed the door, and did what I had never, by night or day, done before, locked it. Then I took the pot from the sack, put it on the table, and sat down to look at it, and gloat. But soon I became cool, practical. It was clever. It had given dramatic proof that it worked. It might conceivably be revolutionary in an extremely important section of the British fishing industry: as revolutionary even as the steam trawl. It might conceivably be worth a fortune. But I must not put my hopes too high until I had made that full-size model, netted it, and given it a practical test. Obviously I could not make this model entirely myself. If I got the blacksmith to make it, it would cost money; and I had no money; and no immediate prospect of having money; for my pot-boiler was still no further advanced than it was a week ago. I did not know the blacksmith at Thorpe. While it was possible that he would give me credit, the idea of asking him to do so was not agreeable. I thought suddenly of Willy Coulson. It would not be agreeable to ask him for a loan; yet it seemed there was very little practical difference between putting some groceries down on my account, and, say, one pound cash; and I was in immediate need of groceries. I wanted something to eat that did not imply cooking. At the same time, I might take the lobsters and put them in a pool down the Landing, so that when the tide flowed they could swim back to the oar-weed, none the worse for their adventure ashore.

The thought of the lobsters caught in my pot gave me courage for the main object of my excursion. There was a pleasing humour in the thought that here I was setting out in fear and trembling to borrow a pound note from my grocer when in a few months' time perhaps I might walk in and buy his whole shop! But my courage failed again when, having set the lobster free, I walked up the Road to Willy Coulson's shop: for Willy, despite that he lacked the characteristic dourness, that he was 'educated', that his shop manners were agreeable to the point of suavity, belonged to one of the oldest and wealthiest seafaring families in the place; and was as 'Bramblewick' at heart as the Fosdycks. I was surprised, however, at the readiness, the eagerness with which he complied with my request. He took a note from his till, and handed it to me over his counter with a tin of sardines and another tin of fags, as nonchalantly as if it had been a coupon receipt: and he asked me agreeably if I had caught any fish this morning, as he had seen me going down the Slipway with Marney Lunn. Yet I had the uncomfortable sensation that as soon as my back was turned, Willy would be smiling the 'Bramblewick' smile, and I had a powerful regret that I was in debt to him at all.

The sight of my pot on the table, however, instantly dispelled all gloomy thoughts. There was no point in my hurrying to the blacksmith, for he would be at dinner. I had still to work out the details of what I wished him to make. I lighted the fire, put the kettle on, then turned eagerly to the pot. I erected it and collapsed it several times, and each time my admiration grew. What I admired most about it was its simplicity: and I was thinking not only of the present model but of the full-size, practical, marketable design. How different it was from dad's collapsible sketching easel! This, which had overshadowed my mother's life for many years, and which she had ironically nicknamed dad's One-man-Band, was an apparatus designed to replace the clumsy folding easel then in vogue among landscape artists. In its early stages it consisted of a wood tray, similar to that used by railway platform newsvendors; and in action this tray was similarly slung round the artist's shoulders by a strap. The easel was hinged to the outer edge of the tray, and when folded lay inside it. In action, however, it could be raised up and extended and adjusted to the size of the canvas or drawing block, and kept in position by two lateral struts. At this stage, despite a tendency for the tray to fall inwards, whenever the artist relaxed the supporting tension of his stomach muscles, the apparatus was tolerably successful; and it had absorbed in its construction nothing more than a paint box, two ordinary easels, and a folding-chair. But dad was not satisfied. He discovered that after an hour's work his muscles were not capable of maintaining that tension; that if he sat down the strap no longer functioned, and the easel lost stability. He discovered also, by an unsought-for experiment, that the whole apparatus was an awkward thing to have attached to your person when you were being pursued across a field by an infuriated bull. He gave his easel folding-legs, adapting for this purpose the tripod of his camera. He disembowelled the camera and used its various parts for improving the easel itself. He added gadgets for holding his water tin, brushes and paints; and at last incorporated in the whole structure a sunshade, and a folding-stool. This stool, later, he detached. Apart from a new paint-box it formed the sole equipment for his sketching expeditions after he had rediscovered that it was much easier to paint with your canvas or block on your knees, and your colours on the ground.

I must remember dad's easel I thought, as I opened and closed my pot again. I must beware of dad's passion for gadgets and for elaboration. It was the same with his painting. Given a subject with a simple composition, such as a strip of beach, an expanse of sunlit scaur and the sea, or a haystack with a turnip field or a patch of bracken, or just a stretch of moor with a road winding over it, he would produce, in a matter of minutes, something that was to me at least of extraordinary beauty. And then, at the very moment when he should have laid down his brushes some devil would possess him, and he would paint a gull or a ship or a coble sail into the glowing spaces of his seascape; or put a horse and cart into his turnip field; or completely ruin the romantic loneliness of the moorland road with a flock of sheep.

Yet, as I examined the structure of my model, I saw with satisfaction that what improvements I made in the full-size pot would make it simpler still. The neat little bolt on the erecting bar would be simpler than a piece of string, and would lock the pot in a single operation. I did not like the look of the piece of iron Marney had lashed in for ballast. I saw suddenly that if instead of having a wood base I made a rectangular frame of angle iron similar to that used for the girders of a bed, and have this frame with iron slats in it so as to form a grid, I could at once provide for the hinging of my bows, and at the same time dispense with ballast altogether. I looked at the pot with a new excitement. Angle iron was terrifically strong. It was used for bridges, for cranes, for building skyscrapers, and all engineering construction where strength combined with lightness was essential. If my pot was thus made, was I not achieving the double purpose of a collapsible pot, and one which, even if subjected to the pounding of rough seas would resist destruction? I gasped. I had invented not only a collapsible pot but an indestructible pot; something with which one could defy the sea itself; and by making it, all except the net of iron or steel, it would actually be *lighter* than a hazel pot, and thus achieve a new saving in the labour and time of hauling.

I lit a fag to steady my nerves. I saw for the first time the certain value of my invention. Here was no fantastic machine for changing base metal into gold, or for achieving perpetual motion, but a practical device that would be a new weapon in the hands of the fisherman in his conflict with the sea: a device that would revive a dying industry; that would, if properly exploited give work to a vast number of my fellow-countrymen, not only at sea, but in the unemployment-stricken areas ashore; and would incidentally provide financial succour for myself. It was a device suggested and already approved by an expert. Marney and John Lunn might exaggerate for dramatic effect: Henry Lunn never. Yet if I was to make a practical success out of it, it must be patented and the secret of it kept until full protection was secured.

The fag made me feel sick. I realized my hunger. The kettle had long since boiled however, and I made some tea and started my breakfast-lunch of bread and sardines, but with the pot still in front of me. My spirits, damped momentarily by the thought of my hampering poverty, quickly rose again. I remembered a lady friend in London, who was a great friend of a well-known City man, who specialized in the commercial development of inventions, and who also was a philanthropist particularly interested in the welfare of ex-soldiers and sailors. If I wrote to my friend giving a brief description of the pot, mentioning its social aspects, and explaining that I required funds and technical advice for the securing of a patent, I knew at least that the matter would be brought to the notice of the great man without delay, and would be regarded as confidential. I would not be asking for charity; any financial help I received would be regarded as an investment in the pot itself, to be repaid a thousand fold from its profits.

I wrote the letter. Then I put it on one side and made a rough scale drawing of the bows and the two bars and my little locking bolt. It would not be wise, I thought, to have the bottom made by the blacksmith, despite his presumable ignorance of lobster pots. This, possibly I could make myself, if I could borrow the requisite tools. It was now nearly one o'clock. I popped my lunch things in the formalin solution, carefully locked the pot away in a cupboard, and with my drawing in my breast pocket, and the letter in my hand lest I should forget to post it, I was ready to go. There were two doors to the street; I locked them both behind me.

The path to Thorpe lay past the midden, and up a little wooded valley called Marner Dale; then over several level pasture fields, the last of these divided by the railway line, which avoids the village itself, and curves round by the Parish Church to Up-Bank Bramblewick. The weather was still mild but dull. The southerly wind had dropped. The sky was overcast and an autumnal haze lay upon the calming sea and upon the hills, shrouding the woods and the brackeny copses so that all the bright colours of yesterday were grey and dead. But I heard a robin singing in the hedgerow, and the gay twittering of a wren; and as I crossed the railway line the sound of the blacksmith's anvil rang through the still air like a cheerful bell.

The smithy was on the extreme outskirts of the village on a lane leading southwards to Garry Beck Dale. It was an ancient building, and in my own memory there had been several smiths. I had been told that the present one had been in occupation only a few months, having come from some distant inland village: and this I thought was extremely lucky for he would be even less likely to know anything about pots.

The place had the customary divided doors, and the top half was open. I leaned my head inside. The smith was standing in front of the forge, working the bellows with one hand, and holding something in the fire with the other; and as I looked he turned, brought a thick piece of white hot iron to the anvil and began to hammer it violently. He was a youngish man, with immense shoulders and arms, and an extraordinarily masterful, clean-shaven face, and fine teeth. Clearly he was unaware of my presence, for in a deep, growling voice he was talking to the piece of iron, which he was shaping into a hook; cursing it, cajoling it, to each blow of the hammer, and finally thrusting it back into the fire with a truculent shout.

'Get back there you b—r, and get yourself hot!'

I opened the bottom door and stepped inside. The one small window was thickly festooned with sooty cobwebs, and masked by a rack of tools. The only light came from the forge, now glowing fiercely in the blast of the bellows which the smith pumped with his left hand. Apart from a narrow gangway between the forge and the anvil, the entire floor was littered with rusty ploughs, harrows, mowing machines, domestic mangles, frames of bicycles, cartwheels, rods and bars of iron, and old horse-shoes. Of these the red fire light made a fantastic pattern, and it threw the smith himself into a silhouette outlined in red, with the shadow of a Herculean smith projected on the ceiling and the farther wall.

He turned again and saw me. But he swore more violently as he hammered the piece of burning iron; as though it were a living thing with a stubborn spirit which he must tame. Then, with a final thwack that would have felled an ox, he sent the thing clattering on to the stone floor, and looking at me, said in a surprisingly gentle voice:

'Now then. Do you want summat?'

I took the drawing from my pocket, but the fire had

106

died, leaving the place almost in darkness, and we had to move to the doorway to look at it. I had drawn a front elevation of the pot minus the bottom; an end elevation, showing the bows, and a more detailed sketch of the locking catch. I explained this to the smith. He listened in silence, with a grimy hand stroking his chin, and his mouth slightly agape. I went on to suggest that he should make one of the bows, putting the kink in first, then the hinging hooks at each end, and finally bending the whole thing to shape. He still said nothing, but he suddenly took the drawing from my hand, turned so as to get a better light on it, and again scratched his chin. Then he growled, almost truculently,

'What is it—what's it for?'

I had been prepared for curiosity, but not for this rude inquisitiveness. He was glaring at me as though he suspected I was playing a practical joke. He rattled me. I felt like telling him to go to the devil with his bad manners and walking off. But my fever to see the job done, to produce the final proof of the success of my invention compelled discretion; and there was something almost hypnotic in his immensity, his bullying masterfulness. I yielded him a half lie.

'It's a sort of trap,' I said.

He looked at the drawing again, his mouth still gaping.

'A trap?' he muttered slowly. 'It's a queer sort of trap. What's it for, to catch foxes?'

He tempted me into a sudden and perhaps too picturesque invention. I had read somewhere of an expedition setting out into the wilds of Africa to trap monkeys and other small mammals: and that its equipment included a number of folding traps, specially designed to prevent injury to the creatures they caught. It *was* a trap for animals, I told the smith; to be used for scientific purposes. But I added sharply:

'Do you think you can do it?'

He swung round and answered quite mildly:

'Do it? I can make anything I have a mind to make in iron; but when a chap comes along with a plough to mend, there's the plough, and there's the thing that's broken, and I know where I am, and it's my own fault if I do it wrong. I can make anything out of iron so long as I know what I'm making, and what it's for. How thick do you want these hoops?'

He gave me back the drawing; then turned, and with a muttered curse, seized hold of a harrow weighing at least a hundredweight that was on the floor, and heaved it bodily into a far corner of the smithy. Then he pulled from under a cartwheel a length of rusty iron rod.

'It's three-eighths, this stuff,' he explained. 'Will it do?'

I had only approximated the thickness of iron which was to supplant the inch-thick hazels of the hazel pot; and I thought that three-eighths of an inch would give me an immense superiority in strength. I approved.

'Have you reckoned what length there is to each hoop?'

'One yard,' I answered.

He took a ruler from his pocket and marked off three lengths with a piece of chalk. Then he held the rod over a chisel fixed edge upwards in the anvil, and cut off the three lengths with three single blows of the hammer. He picked up one length and came to the door again.

'What about that kink? Let's see the plan again. It comes fair in the middle doesn't it?'

He strode back to the anvil, put the rod on the chisel edge, and see-sawed it until it balanced. He chalked the balancing point, laid the rod on the anvil so that the mark came over a small square hole, put a blunt piece of iron on the mark, and gave it a violent blow. The kink, which in my thin parrot-cage wire had taken me an hour to make, was made. In less than another five minutes he had turned the two ends: he put the whole thing over the curved part of the anvil then, and pulled it into a perfect semicircle. One bow was finished. It seemed to me that it had taken less time and scarcely more energy than the cutting of a single hazel stick.

I was thrilled. I forgave the smith his bad manners. He was a craftsman; and what was his seeming rudeness but the bursting self-confidence of youth, in his strength and ability and independence! Marney was like that, and John. And Henry himself was not without conceit and self-assertiveness and a bravado towards life; although in him there was that tempering cynicism, that lurking self-mistrust, which age and experience alone can give.

He threw the finished bow on to the bench, and without a word started another. In less than half an hour the three bows were made. Placed on top of each other, there was scarcely a hair's-breadth difference in shape between them.

'What about those other gadgets?' the smith demanded then. 'What do you want them made of?'

For the wire coupling and erecting bars of the original

pot I had substituted in my drawing two flat iron bars: the coupling bar to be turned over at both ends, to move freely in the kinks of the bows it coupled, but having near the middle bow a slot to hold the catch, which was to be riveted to the free end of the erecting bar. The other end of the erecting bar would of course move in the kink of the remaining bow.

The smith took a glance at the drawing, then rummaged among the debris again, and produced a length of flat bar, an inch wide and a quarter thick. It looked exactly right. He cut off two measured lengths. Then he seized the beam of the bellows and pumped. The fire, which had died away, burst into life, filling the smithy with a fierce, scintillating illumination. He thrust one of the bars into the fire and raked cinders on to it. He brought it out with its end white hot, and put it on the anvil point: and with his hammer coaxed it gently round until it formed a half-closed hook. He laid it on one side and proceeded to heat the other bar. It did not take him long to form two half closed hooks on this one, which was to be the coupling bar. Then he turned to the first one again, heated the untouched end and punched a small hole through it. He rummaged on the floor and produced a short square piece of iron.

'That will make your catch,' he said, gripping it with the fire tongs. 'I'll rivet that in, then make the hole for it to fit in, in that other gadget, then we'll fix 'em to the hoops and the job's done.'

He started to blow at the bellows again, and became almost conversational as he did so.

'I can make almost anything in iron,' he said. 'Almost

anything. But I shouldn't like to mess on with jobs like this very often. I don't like working with thin stuff. I like something you can get hold of, and bray with a big hammer. Summat you can fight!'

He took the small piece of iron out, and began tapping it, and I could see what restraint there was in that gentle tapping, what curbing of strength and desire. But as I watched the bolt take shape, I was thinking what an admirable material iron was for my purpose: what an immense advantage it gave over wood. The three-eighths of an inch thickness of my bows would surely be as strong as five times that thickness of hazel. Protect it from rust, and even in the worst weather nothing could happen to it, unless perhaps it got dented or bent; and it would be easy enough to bend it back to shape if that did happen. And the making of an iron pot seemed so comparatively easy. Metal did not split. With proper tools you could shape it as you wished, and yet preserve its strength and rigidity. It seemed that there remained only the question of cost, and that did not seriously trouble me. Iron could not be impossibly dear if the smith could allow tons of it to lie rusting in his smithy. Yet I felt thankful for change from the pound note I had in my pocket; for I had little idea how smiths made their charges.

He finished the catch and riveted it to the end of the erecting bar. He punched a square hole in the coupling bar and filed it out until the catch fitted snugly. He tapped round the half-closed hooks without heating them. There was nothing more to do. I offered him a fag which he lit with a cinder he pulled from the fire with his tongs. He then collected the parts and brought them to the doorway, and again he reminded me of Marney, for there was admiration in the way he looked at them.

'Aye,' he remarked, scratching his chin again. 'There's not much to choose between these three hoops. But I still can't quite see how a thing like this is going to catch animals. But maybe this isn't all of it.'

I caught the inquisitive look in his eyes again, but I was not to be drawn. I asked him how much I had to pay him; and to my surprise he looked embarrassed.

'Damned if *I* know,' he growled. 'Damned if *I* know. I've never done a job like that before the whole time I've been a smith.' He scratched at his chin thoughtfully for a while. 'We've been about an hour at it. I reckon my time at one-and-six an hour, seeing I'm my own boss. Then there's material. Call it a couple of bob.'

My heart leapt, as a woman's might, at finding some astounding bargain at a sale. Two shillings for making the most difficult part of a collapsible, indestructible lobster pot; and a single model at that! And a hazel pot would cost at least five! I had an impulse to put a ten shilling note in the smith's hand, but remembered my urgent poverty, and gave him four: and I left him scratching his skin and gaping.

I walked across the fields carrying the frame under my coat. The light was failing. The short grass was drenched with dew. I hurried. I had the bottom to make before I could be positive as to the success of the whole contraption. I would have to borrow some tools too; a drill, some hack-saw blades, and if possible, another vice. I did not want to see Marney again until the whole frame was complete for netting; and I thought it would be a very good idea if I bought some steak from the butcher's and grilled it over my fire, and got some fried potatoes when the fish-shop opened. Then I would have no dirty pans and a minimum of crockery to wash up. The thought of the steak was a pleasant one, but not more pleasant than the picture I had of the completed full-size pot, netted and ready for its first trial; and the sense I had that I was already measuring myself against the strength of the sea.

8

I put the frame under my table, locked both doors again and hurried down to buy my meat. I saw no sign of the Lunns. I walked from the butcher's round to the gas-house, and borrowed from the foreman a breast drill, a set of bits, some saw blades, and a round file. I deposited these in the cottage, locked the doors again, and walked across to the midden, behind which I was confident of finding some bed girders. Unfortunately the green in addition to being the playground is also the village drying ground; and a tall, sombrely-dressed woman was removing some clothes from a line close to the very place where I hoped the girders would be. Her name was Jane Allison. She was the daughter of an old Bramblewick sea-captain, who had been drowned before he had made 'brass', and Jane (who evidently had been a fine-looking girl in her day) had devoted herself to looking after her mother. This had given her a rather morbid outlook on life. Her mind seemed to dwell perpetually on funerals, and other matters connected with the dead and the dying. She seemed to find a peculiar pleasure in hearing about and talking about 'folks being took bad', the signs and symptoms and progress of fatal maladies, and the details of difficult and abnormal confinements. But what I found trying about Jane was her habit of making a fatuous remark whenever I met her, a remark that obviously had no connection with her inner thoughts, although it proved her capable of a peculiarly keen superficial observation. Thus if I was in my sea boots and carrying a fishing rod she would say in her deep slow melancholy voice that was so admirably modulated for the communication of bad news:

'Now then. Are you going fishing?'

Or if I had a loaf of bread in my hand:

'Now then. Have you just been to the bakers?'

Or if I was coming back across the green with my empty ash buckets, and it was raining:

'Now then. Have you just been to the midden. It's raining isn't it?'

And apart from this, Jane was 'Bramblewick.' She had the 'Bramblewick' way of looking at you when she spoke: the 'Bramblewick' smile, and the 'Bramblewick' inquisitiveness. I did not fancy her watching me now poking behind the midden, and then remarking:

'Now then. Are you looking for summat?'

I steered across the southern edge of the green, and wandered impatiently about until she had filled her clothes-basket and disappeared. Then, glad that it was dusk, I searched the bushes and soon discovered two bed girders of standard size. They had clumps of cast-iron welded to their ends, with tongues to fit into the front and back of the bed to which they belonged. And as the beds were of the old-fashioned, all-metal type they were fitted with a number of thick metal studs, for securing the movable steel lattices. The hack-saw blades I had borrowed however, were new, and I did not anticipate serious difficulty in sawing off the ends and these studs. All I wanted in the way of material now was the flat bars to be fastened across the frame when finished to make it into a grid. I continued my search and at last pulled out of a clump of dead nettles the skeleton of a folding baby carriage, made almost entirely of the required material; shaped it was true, and riveted and hinged in many places, but not so securely that it would not yield to my saw, and then be straightened out. But I decided that as I should not need this until the final stage of manufacture, it would be best to leave it where it was until dark: for if I was seen carrying it Bramblewick might be crediting me with a more interesting activity even than the making of a lobster pot. I moved with the bed girders to the edge of the green and, satisfied that the lane was deserted, I hurried into my washhouse, and closed the door. But I had no sooner lit the gas than I heard footsteps on the cobbles outside. They stopped at the cottage door, and I heard someone trying the latch. I stepped out and found John.

'Hello,' he said, 'I didn't think of your being down there, I thought I'd look in for a minute or two, and see what the smith had made for you.'

I hurried him into the washhouse; for he had a powerful voice; and the Brewster's front door had just opened, and I was alarmed by his remarks. He went on to alarm me more.

'Aye,' he said. 'I've just been up to the station to see if some mussels had come, and I met the Thorpe smith on his bicycle. He told me he'd been making a queer sort of trap for you, although he wasn't quite certain who you were. He told me it was a trap to catch wild animals and he asked me if you were going out foreign. I reckon that was smart to put him off the truth like that. I couldn't help laughing to myself though, thinking what it really was. But it shows you how things get about in a spot like this, doesn't it.'

I agreed; and I asked John apprehensively if he had mentioned lobster pots to the smith. He answered indignantly:

'No damned fear. I just pretended to be completely ignorant. But he's a very decent chap is the smith. And he seemed to think you'd got your head screwed on the right way, too; only he thought you seemed a bit close and mysterious. Have you got it down here? What's he made?'

I was relieved. But I told John that I was not going to show him the frame until it was finished. He looked disappointed, and slightly huffed, but he quickly recovered.

'All right,' he said. 'That's not the most important thing I came to see you about. I was in the Institute this afternoon; and you know there's a lot of old books in the reading-room. Well, I was just messing on, and I saw a book called the Canadian Year Book: and thinks I, I wonder if there'll be anything about lobsters in it: and damned if I didn't find this!'

John pulled a piece of pencilled paper from his pocket, and read out, dramatically:

'Number of lobsters caught on an average every year in Canadian waters, seventy to ninety millions. Number of pots in use, one and a half millions. Value of pots, one million seven thousand dollars! . . . . What do you think of that, eh? And it's not counting Newfoundland, where there's thousands of boats lobstering for the canneries. And they use almost the same sort of pot as we do. I've seen them. And they lose them just the same way. I've been reckoning that if you got your pot patented and manufactured, and sold it only to give you a profit of a shilling a pot, you'd make a fortune out of Canada alone. A million shillings is fifty thousand quid. God, it's enough to take your breath away!'

It was. But I repressed the excitement that was already rising in me again; and I wished that John would go and let me get on with the job; and I gave him a hint by asking him if he would tell Marney not to call on me this evening: that I would bring the frame round to him as soon as it was ready for netting. John moved to the door, and turning, paused.

'Well, I'll not be staying,' he said. 'I thought you'd like to know about those figures. And, by the way, there was just one other thing I wanted to tell you: I didn't mention it in the warehouse because I knew father would only start being sarcastic. I saw that chap in Burnharbour last night. He said we could start a band for under fifty quid:

and there's a chap here, a Bramblewick chap, one of the finest cornet players on the whole of this coast, only he's a bit out of practice through not playing in a band for a long time, whose already half promised to be conductor. I'm going round now to see a few chaps I know. I bet anything we'll have a band going before the winter's out.'

He went, and as soon as his footsteps had died away, I hurried into the cottage, collected the frame and the tools, came back and locked the washhouse door behind me. I could dispense with tea, and combine this with my steak later on. I would first saw the ends and the rivets from the girders. Then cut two lengths of two feet for the sides, and two of one and a half feet for the ends of the rectangular frame. These I would rivet together at each corner. I would need only one cross-bar (of the baby carriage iron) and the slats (from the same source, and seven in number) would be riveted from end to end, and thus form the grid.

Angle iron is simply a strip of metal folded along its length at right angles, so that its section is the letter L. At this stage of my mechanical education I could not have explained with the exact scientific formulæ why it was so immensely strong. I knew it by instinct, as one knows that a tapering buttress supporting a church wall is stronger than a straight one and that a hollow bamboo is stronger than a solid stem. I did not know that the term angle iron describes the shape and not necessarily the material, being applied indiscriminately to both iron and steel: and I did not know that the material used for bed girders was steel: not the steel of battleships it was true, nor the steel of cutlery, but a material appreciably tougher and less tractable than the wrought iron used by smiths. Only when I moved the hack-saw across the edge of the first girder, near to its end, and drew from it a penetrating squeal that sent a shiver down my spine and put my teeth on edge did I suspect what labour lay before me before even my material was ready for the drilling of the holes to take the rivets and hinge the bows.

9

I was to learn that there are machines with which a boy can shear a piece of angle iron, twice the thickness of my girders, with the mere pressure of a hand; and punch holes through the same material, as though it were cardboard. It took me until eight o'clock to saw off the ends of one girder and remove the studs; and by that time I was near the point of physical exhaustion. I went into the cottage, lighted the fire, put the kettle on, and got my potatoes from the fried-fish shop. The meal revived me; but I heard the Brewsters going to bed before I had got my two long sections and one end-piece cut from the first girder; and I had still to cut the remaining piece from girder number two.

A hack-saw is an entirely different tool from the saw used for cutting wood. The handle is straight, giving one no real grip, the strokes must be short so that one can use only the muscles of one's forearm, and the blade is so thin and brittle that the slightest misdirection will cause it to snap. The sound too, even when the blade is deep in a cut is high-pitched, rasping, and unpleasant. Yet I found an ever-growing satisfaction in my labour. The toughness of the metal increased my confidence in its ability to withstand the destructiveness of the sea. I could hear the faint roar of the smoothing surf whenever I was obliged to pause and rest my arm: not as we had heard it in the hazel copse; yet with a new and personal challenge in it; and, as I laboured a profound revelation came to me. I was creating something which if it fulfilled the promise of the first small model, would put new and vigorous life into the moribund inshore fishing industry, that would remove the blight of unemployment from the young men of the coast, and save the magnificent breed of them which the sea had fostered from extinction. Prosperity would come again to these old villages and ports like Bramblewick and Burnharbour. New boats would be needed. New boats would be built, and stimulation given to another dying craft. The making of the pots would employ more men; iron and coal miners; iron makers, the actual makers of the frame; the makers of twine and rope and so on in an ever expanding circle. And if the new and intensive method of fishing which my invention made possible resulted in heavier catches than the ordinary market could absorb; why shouldn't the lobsters be canned, and still a new British industry come into existence?

Was there not in this something infinitely more noble than the writing of a book? Supposing even that my book *was* to be a work of art? Edison, Marconi, Ford, had done a greater service to humanity than all the writers and artists of their age. It might be said that wireless telegraphy was a finer legacy to the civilized world than Hamlet. True that a week ago I would have considered such a statement blasphemy; yet only, I thought now, from intellectual snobbishness. And was there not, after all, a very close analogy between an invention and a work of art? Both in their inception welled up or burst from the subconscious mind by that process called inspiration. Both were the products of the registered facts, the observations taken in and stored during a period of lying fallow. I saw in a flash that while I had imagined that I had lain fallow waiting for the inspiration of my book, for the bursting of the latent creative force within me, it was this thing that I had been subconsciously preparing for; it was this that had brought me back to Bramblewick, to live among the fishers, to relearn their ways, to comprehend their problems, to hear that fighting challenge in the roar of the sea. I recognized in all of this, in my inability to complete my pot-boiler, to stay indoors, or resist the seductive proposals of Marney Lunn, or to keep away from the sea, the workings of the destiny that shapes our ends.

I was not a writer. I was an inventor, an engineer, a potential captain of industry. And the sudden realization that the pot-boiler was no longer on my conscience; that I need not give another thought to the worrying complexities of my unstarted book, brought a great joy to my heart, a new energy to my aching muscles. I sawed at the last remaining stud until the hack-saw blade was almost red hot, knocked the stud out with a violent blow of my hammer, and put the four sections of angle iron together on the table in the shape of the frame. I measured and marked the position for the holes, and began drilling them without stopping to rest.

I had never drilled a piece of metal before. I learnt quickly that with a breast drill it was infinitely more difficult and strenuous than sawing, although it brought a greater variety of muscles into play. At the top of the drill is a curved metal plate, the shape of a crutch. This is pressed against your chest while with one hand you keep the drill on the mark, and with the other turn the geared handle. As a relief to the intense pain produced by the pressure of the crutch on your chest, it may be operated from the stomach muscles, and from various inter-lying regions of the anatomy, although the pain is only transferred and there is a loss of mechanical efficiency.

I had four rivet holes to drill in each length; six holes to take the ends of the bows, eight to give security to the netting, sixteen to take the slats and the cross-piece, a total of forty-six; and the slats and the cross-piece would require a further twenty-nine, a grand total of seventy-five! But I was confident that this intensive labour would be unnecessary when the thing was manufactured: probably the whole base would be cast or stamped out of a metal sheet in a single operation; and my determination to complete the frame before I went to bed, was not checked by the thought that I had the baby carriage to dissect and straighten and cut into lengths before I started to drill it. I laboured furiously. I mastered pain. I mastered fatigue. I was quite oblivious to the passing of time. Yet I knew by the position of the moon when I went out for the baby carriage that it was already long past midnight. I met the friendly cat. It was flirting however, and did not follow me back. I discovered that the baby carriage was, like the parrot cage, surprisingly well made; and that like the bed girders it was made of something tougher than blacksmith's iron; but I rejoiced in the thought of the extra strength this would give, and I tackled it with redoubled fury. I had not only cut and straightened the strips, but drilled the holes in them before I began the final and exciting task of assembly.

I had no doubt whatever that the thing would work as well as the small model: for the only real difference between the two was the locking catch. My excitement was almost an æsthetic excitement. I wanted to see how the thing looked in full scale, closed and open, to get the architectural effect of the complete apparatus.

Although I understood the technique of cold riveting I had no more practical experience of it than I had of drilling. Here, however, I had no unpleasant discovery, for it consisted of little else than strenuous but straight-forward hammering. The first rivet secured a side length and an end length together as though they had been welded, and with the second rivet in, I knew that I had made a joint that no conceivable movement of the sea could rend asunder. I used the top of the ancient gas-stove as an anvil. I must have made a devilish racket; and there was once, when I was hunting on the floor for a dropped rivet, that I imagined I heard the Brewster's baby crying, and the remonstrating voice of Reub himself; but if I had been waking the whole of

123

Bramblewick I could not have stopped now. I finished the four corners of the frame. Without the cross-piece it looked strong enough to support a weight of at least a ton. Yet except for the time it took me to recover from a severe attack of cramp in my hammering arm, I did not waste time admiring it. I riveted the crosspiece on. I began to rivet the seven slats. At last I put the whole thing down upon the table—done.

I was exhausted. My hands were blistered and raw: my right arm felt as though it had passed between the rollers of a mangle: I had such a pain in my back that I groaned when I tried to straighten it. But I kept my back bent. I lit a fag: and using my comparatively untired left hand, I put the hooked ends of the uncoupled bow into their respective holes. I kept it in the collapsed position, and keeping them flat too, so as not to anticipate the effect, I put the other two bows into position. They fitted perfectly. I seized the end of the erecting bar, moved its bow upright. I raised the other two, pressed the catch into its hole, and let go. And once more I gasped with admiration.

It seemed to me at once that I had created a perfect thing. It looked perfect. The bows looked slender, but the arch of them was as suggestive of strength as the slender arch of a well designed bridge rising from perfectly proportioned foundations. It looked right. It *looked* right, I knew, because it *was* right. It was strong, strong as it possibly could be within the conditions of utility. It was simple. There was not a piece of metal in it, or a shape, that did not fulfil a necessary purpose. And above all, it worked. I released the catch. The bows fell, and lay

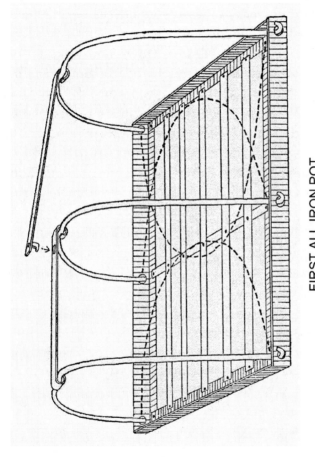

FIRST ALL IRON POT

Showing bows erect, and locking bolt about to be inserted. Dotted lines
show position of bows when collapsed

neatly inside the angle iron frame. I erected it again. The catch clicked home and held the whole thing secure as the keystone of an arch. Nothing remained but the net. It was inconceivable that the net could make more than the slightest difference to these two quite easy operations. I had already proved this with the first model.

I had a sudden wild desire to go and wake up the Lunns: to show it to them: to have them share my triumph: but I knew I would have to wait. I thought I had best light the cottage fire again, and make some tea, wash, and then sit by the fire and rest. As I opened the washhouse door however, I was amazed to find that it was almost daylight; and I heard a peculiar rumbling sound from the Dock: the sound of the cobles being launched. I went into the cottage, put the pot under the table, pulled on my sea-boots, and having locked the doors again, hurried down. The moon was setting, and the indications of dawn as yet were only slight. It was almost dark in the Dock, which at first glance seemed deserted. But as I approached the Slipway top, I distinguished the figures of the three Lunns, and Luke and Tindal Fosdyck and their nephew Tom, walking up it. They had already launched the Fosdycks' coble to the shore. They walked quietly, and there was something indescribably surreptitious in the soft *pad-pad* of their rubber boots on the paving. They gathered round the Lunns' coble, which was on its launching wheels behind the breakwater. Someone knocked the chocks from under the wheels. I moved to help, and found myself alongside Marney Lunn on the boat's gunwale, as she was swung round and headed for the Slipway.

He did not speak or give me the slightest sign of recognition. No one spoke. There seemed a peculiar tenseness in the air; a compelled silence. Only the coble wheels made a noise, and this seemed to be checked as much as possible.

I felt that I had joined a party of raiders, preparing a surprise attack on a watchful enemy. Even when we stopped the boat alongside the other one, with the wheels awash in the incoming tide, no one spoke. The lashings of the wheels were cast off. The coble was launched and the wheels were hauled to safety up the Slipway, and the Lunns and the Fosdyck family began hurriedly to carry their lines and other gear to their respective cobles. I helped the Lunns, but not one of them spoke to me or gave any sign that they were aware either of my help or my existence. I watched both boats put off and disappear in the gloom which still shrouded the sea: the Fosdycks rowing, the Lunns moving more quickly under power. The air was still and extremely mild. From the invisible scaur ends there came only the faintest sound of surf. But in the very stillness of the air, the calmness of the sea, I sensed an enmity, a sinister intent. They were raiders these men. They were setting off on a sortie to the very outposts of the enemy. I knew this autumn weather; these treacherous lulls. With the rising of the sun a wind might spring up from the east, raising in less than an hour a swell, which, breaking on the scaurs and across the Landing Mouth, would compel the boats to make a swift and perilous retreat, cutting their lines perhaps, and forgoing their booty of fish, so nearly won. It was hard, dangerous, ill-paid work, I thought; a gamble, with the odds too heavily weighted against the fishers. Yet it had the fascination of all gambles, of all elemental conflicts: and I was profoundly stirred by the thought that from now on I was joining arms against the sea with a new and cunning weapon.

I moved up the Slipway, into the still silent village. I was hungry, but not sleepy. I would have breakfast, and rest in front of the fire, until the boats came back; and I would carefully examine every detail of the pot, and make doubly certain of its perfection, before I got Marney to put the netting on. And it would be a fine gesture to fortune I thought, if I lit my fire with the pages of my abandoned short story.

10

I awoke with a shock to find myself in my arm-chair, fully dressed, and still in my sea-boots. The fire was out. Although the window blind was up, it was almost dark in the room. I looked at my watch and found it was half-past four in the afternoon. I must have fallen asleep immediately after breakfast, and slept throughout the whole day.

I got up hastily and looked out of the window. It was raining and blowing hard. But I could see from the slant of the rain that the wind was south-west, and I had no fear for the boats, which must have come home many hours ago. I looked at my pot. It was lying erect upon the table among the breakfast things. I was hungry and stiff and cold; but the sight of the pot was a swift stimulant. Marney Lunn would just be starting tea. I would go round to him at once. I remembered the need for caution, however. I collapsed the pot, and made a neat parcel of it in brown paper. Feeling in my pocket for my pen-knife, I encountered coins, and experienced a sudden sense of opulence. On my way round I would call at Willy's and buy some chocolates for Amy, and a tin of fags for Marney himself.

The wind was stronger than I had thought, and the rain was torrential. Having made my purchases, I hurried down to the deserted Dock. Both boats were safe behind the breakwater, and I had been right in judging the direction of the wind to be south-west and off-shore, for the sea made no sound that was audible above that of the wind and the lashing rain. There was a light in Marney's window. I opened the door and stepped inside, and at once I was glad that I had taken the precaution to wrap up the pot, for Tom Fosdyck was sharing the fireside with Marney, who was holding the baby while Amy was laying the table for tea.

Tom Fosdyck somehow did not fit into my composite portrait of the seafaring Bramblewicker. True that he possessed most of the Bramblewick characteristics. He was, like his uncles, powerfully built, and he had the same broad type of face, with strong cheek bones, and eyes that were less blue than the Lunns'. He had the typical dourness too, rarely speaking unless spoken to, and then usually in gruff monosyllables. He was the same age as Marney. They had gone to school together.

They had been ship-mates on several long voyages abroad, and there was a peculiar friendship between them which, on the pure Bramblewick man's part, amounted I believed to an almost dog-like admiration and affection: and in this was included Amy and the 'bairn'. There was scarcely a night, in winter time at any rate, that Tom, who was unmarried, did not 'look in', and while he usually refused to share a meal, he would sit for hours smoking his pipe, just watching Marney and Amy at their fireside jobs, listening to Marney yarning, yet saying nothing himself but a very occasional 'Aye'. What Marney got out of the friendship, beyond an audience for his yarning I could not guess, for I had observed that he never took advantage of it to pump Tom as to the activities of the Fosdyck camp: in fact it seemed an implied condition of this fraternization of members of rival families, that professional matters, except in their widest aspects, should not be discussed at all. It was clear however that in ordinary circumstances Tom was a welcome guest; and if Marney conveyed a warning to me in a quick, subtle look, which embraced my parcel and the figure of Tom, who sat with his back towards me, there was no animosity in it. I skilfully placed the pot in a corner just inside the door, before I moved towards the fireplace. Amy smiled pleasantly, and Marney, with just another sly glance towards Tom, as though to assure himself that my manœuvre had not been noticed, remarked with an innocent grin:

'Hello. You're just in time for a cup of tea. Get your oilskins off and sit down.'

I removed my oilskin coat and sat down at the

table. Tom, who had not turned, started to fill his pipe methodically. I saw that Marney was watching him, and that Amy, too, gave him a glance out of the tail of her eye, as she moved busily between the pantry and the table. None of us spoke, yet if Tom Fosdyck's mind had been susceptible to thought transference, he would have been aware that the air was charged with vibrating messages imploring him to complete the lighting of his pipe, light it, and go. Clearly he had not that sort of a mind; or some perverse devil possessed him, for he suddenly put his pipe in his pocket, and turning to Amy said:

'Did you say I *was* to have a cup of tea, Amy?'

'You know you're welcome, without being asked,' Amy answered with an admirable readiness.

'Aye. Of course,' added Marney, not quite so skilfully. 'We're all ready, aren't we? I'd best put the bairn in its cradle.'

As Marney moved to do so, he gave me and the parcel another secret glance. But the pot if its revelation was to be delayed was safe in its wrapping, and we began the meal. The atmosphere, however, was constrained. Personally, while I liked Tom Fosdyck, I could never rid myself of the feeling that he was at heart 'Bramblewick'; I could never feel completely at ease in his company. I was itching to show Marney the pot, and I knew that Marney was itching to see it; and there was the more depressing thought that Tom, having stayed to tea, was likely enough to stay on.

I asked Marney how they had done with their fishing.

'We got two and a half baskets,' he answered. 'The Fosdycks got two, but you had one less line than us, hadn't you, Tom?'

Tom was busy with a cheese-cake.

'Aye,' he answered.

'It turned mucky soon after daybreak,' Marney went on. 'It looked as though it was going to blow north-east again. But it didn't.'

'It's blowing hard enough now,' said Amy, *'and* raining.'

'Aye. And it's good enough to get round north-east yet. What do you say, Tom!'

'Aye,' Tom answered.

There was a lull in this not too entertaining conversation, and then we heard footsteps close under the cottage window, and then a sharp knock at the door. The knock itself was enough to indicate an unusual visitor; for Marney kept open house, and his callers, even the postman and the milkman usually just stepped in.

'What the hell's that?' he muttered, with a glance from the door to Amy.

Amy herself looked startled.

'*I* don't know. You'd best go and see.'

Marney got up. There were two doors, and as the wind was so violent he had to close the inner door behind him. But we heard a voice, and I thought I heard my own name pronounced. This was confirmed when Marney answered:

'Aye. He's here. I'll give it to him.'

The outer door closed again. Marney stepped inside. He was holding a telegram in his hand.

'It's a wire,' he said tensely, looking at me. 'It's for you.'

I was not in the habit of receiving telegrams. There

was something horribly sinister in the appearance of the small buff envelope which Marney handed to me as solemnly as though it had been some holy relic; and the deliberate politeness with which the company proceeded with tea only increased my apprehension. Nor did the contents of the telegram, which I had to read twice before I fully comprehended it, diminish my embarrassment; for the shock produced by good news and bad news can be equally disastrous to one's power of self-control. The telegram was from the lady to whom I had written yesterday. It said that Mr. X. was 'deeply impressed' by my proposals, and that it was of 'utmost importance for me to secure immediate protection'. He would pay all fees and expenses. The necessary forms and a cheque were being posted to me to-day.

I glanced from this exciting document round the table. With a painful politeness my three companions were still concentrating their attention upon their plates. Some explanation was necessary. I stuffed the telegram in my pocket and remarked as nonchalantly as I could:

'It's nothing important.'

I seemed to hear a united sigh of relief. Amy was the first to speak.

'Eh! I *am* glad it's not bad news. It gave me quite a turn.'

'Aye. It did me, too,' put in Marney, showing his relief by passing his cup for some more tea.

'Do you know,' Amy went on. 'I never see someone from the post office going off with a wire but what I think of that day I was standing talking to poor Mrs. Elders up Chapel Street, when the telegraph boy came up with a telegram to say her Tom had been drowned out in China. He was such a cheeky lad they had at the post office then. He just stood there whistling a tune, and then he actually wanted to know if there was a reply. Of course he didn't know what was in the wire, but when she told me, I gave him a stinging slap over his face and told him to be off.'

'I've heard of folks who dropped dead when they *saw* a telegram,' said Marney, 'before they even opened it . . . And yet do you know what I thought first when I gave it to you? Damn it, I thought you'd been having a go at a cross-word puzzle on the sly, and they'd wired you saying you'd won. They *do* send wires to the winners, you know.'

I would have liked to have told Marney then and there that the contents of the telegram were more thrilling in their significance than any conceivable cross-word puzzle prize. But the need for secrecy seemed even stronger now, the presence of Tom Fosdyck even more of a constraint; and as we finished tea, and Tom pulling his pipe from his pocket again, drew his chair round to the fire, I saw that my only chance of getting Marney to himself was to get him to my own cottage. I waited until Tom reached forward to the fire to light a spill. Then, quickly touching Marney's arm, I pointed to the parcel and the door. He gave me a nod of understanding. I got up, put my oilskins on, and pushing the chocolates and the tin of fags across the table, picked up the pot and hurried out, before either Amy or Marney had a chance to recover from the new surprise, or Tom had finished lighting his pipe.

I lighted my gas, and read the telegram again. I

decided that for the time being it would be best to say nothing about it, even to Marney. He was already at the door, and he stepped in, slapping the rain from his short reefer coat. I moved past him and locked both doors.

'God,' he said at once. 'It was a bit of bad luck Tom coming in like that. He scarcely ever comes in until long past tea. John told me last night you were making a full-sized pot. Aye, and Tom himself told us just before you came in, that you'd been up at the blacksmith's yesterday afternoon, and that he'd heard you were going out foreign, on some sort of an expedition to catch wild animals. Have you finished it? I came up here this afternoon, but you'd got the door locked and I couldn't get an answer. Let's have a look at it.'

I removed my breakfast crockery, and put it in the formalin bucket. Then, with the table clear, I undid the parcel. I had no more nervousness about Marney's expert criticism. I took his approval for granted. I erected the pot, and demonstrated how easily the catch worked. I explained the structure of the base, and how, through it being entirely of metal, we could dispense with ballast, and yet have the whole apparatus lighter than a ballasted hazel pot.

'It's champion! It's champion!' he muttered. 'Damn it, even if it *does* get knocked about in a gale it's going *to* take no harm. It's the ballast that smashes up our pots so easily. They start moving about when there's a rough sea, the ballast lashings get chafed through, and the ballast gets loose and just hammers the frame to bits. It's champion!' he repeated enthusiastically. 'I tell you a boat using pots like this is going to make four times as much brass as one using our sort. I only wish we had three fleets of them ready for fishing now. We'd never bait another line. Look at this morning! Two and a half baskets, and lucky if we get eight bob for the lot, and our bait cost ten!. . . Come on,' he added, taking a ball of twine, and a netting needle from his pocket, 'let's get the damned thing netted. I'm dying to see what it looks like, finished. I've got some proper twine, too. I'm going to make a real job of it. Let's have a bit of fire on, and make ourselves cosy. I know it's warm to-night, but I reckon a spot's twice as cheerful when there's a fire in it.'

I lighted the fire and put the kettle on, thinking that I'd wash up while Marney was at work. He settled himself in the bed-chair, with the pot on the floor, resting against his knee. I pulled the settee round to the fire, and sat down waiting for the kettle to boil. But I quickly yielded to the fascination of Marney's moving hands; and when it did boil I took it off, for its noise was nagging. In almost everything creative that he did, Marney revealed himself an artist. He worked under a terrific pressure of mental concentration. He frowned continuously, and screwed his eyes, and his shut lips quivered, as though some leakage of nerve force was being trapped and forced back to perform its proper function. He did not speak. I think that he was quite oblivious to my existence. He had lit a fag, but he had put it on the imitation marble mantelpiece, when he tied the first knot, and I was aware of it smouldering into the paint which hid the honest slate beneath, although I felt quite incapable of reaching up and putting it out. The net grew. The twine was manilla, and much thicker than the line he had used for the small pot. It was in itself a lovely substance, the colour of straw, tightly laid, and very strong. The meshes were bigger, but they were no less even and beautiful. I forgot again that my personal concern was the collapsible and the indestructable frame which he was covering. And I was certain that Marney was equally unconcerned about it, and that he was thinking of nothing but the net, and how it would look when it was done.

It was a bigger task than netting the small pot. He had to stop at frequent intervals and fill his needle. Every joining knot that he made he knotted double, and cut close so that there would be no frayed ends to show; and twice, having apparently decided that a mesh was not precisely what it ought to be, he unknotted a whole row, and did it over again. His concentration became even more intense when he started the first spout. But he made no answering remark when he finished it, and stretched it across, and I told him that it was a beauty. Nor did he speak when he had finished the other, although I knew that he was satisfied that it was an exact replica of the first. Not until he began the doors did he break that tense silence. He paused suddenly, with the first row of clove-hitches half formed.

'You know,' he remarked thoughtfully, 'I'll not say that our old man wasn't right about that door. Our doors have a stick at the top of them, and when you untie them they drop almost of their own weight. But then they're tied to the side sticks, and this pot hasn't got any side sticks. It's the only fault I have to find with it. It would look twice as good if it had side sticks.'

I smiled with a confidence that I had lacked when
Marney had made the same criticism of the small model.
It was by dispensing with the rigid side sticks that the
collapsing of the pot had been made possible; and I had
compensated for their loss by giving the bows and the
two top bars ample strength. I explained this.

'Aye,' Marney agreed. 'I can see we've got to do
without them; but we can't have a stick on the doors; and
say what you like, they're not so good as our doors. It
was the first thing father noticed; and I bet you it will be
the first thing he'll notice in this pot. So long as you tell
him why they've got to be laced, I don't mind. He's as
sharp as a needle for finding a fault in a thing, is our old
man.'

I expressed my willingness to take full responsibility
for the design of the door; and Marney without another
word continued. It was a quick, straightforward job now.
He made both doors, and before he laced up the second
one, he tied the bait string in, and I gave him the
dish-cloth to fix in it as a dummy bait. He tied the door
up, and put the finished pot in the middle of the table.

We both stood up then with our backsides to the fire.
It was not perhaps quite such a thrilling climax as the
completion of the first model. Then there had been the
exciting doubt as to whether the thing would collapse,
and again, whether it would fish. We had proved that it
would do both. It was the look of the thing that
impressed us now; the shape, the æsthetic effect. It was
definitely beautiful; and we shared the satisfaction it
gave us; for the netting, itself beautiful, covered (without
hiding) the frame as successfully as the surface

modelling of a sculpture whose anatomy is right. And there was a deeper reason for our satisfaction, I thought, for the whole apparatus looked supremely fitted for its practical purpose of catching lobsters, and withstanding the tempers of the sea.

We lit fags, and Marney suddenly moved to the pot, and with an artist's gesture trimmed away a ragged end of twine that he had left. Then he stood back again and remarked:

'Well, what do you think of it?'

'I think the netting's champion!' I said fervently.

He flushed.

'Aye. It doesn't look too bad. Not too damned bad. But those bows are a good shape,' he conceded handsomely. 'You couldn't make them so even with hazels. And I like the look of that bed-iron along the bottom, too. It looks champion. I only wish Amy could see it, though,' he added, 'now it's all finished. I tell you what, let's shut it up and wrap it in paper again, and take it back. Tom's almost certain to have gone by now, for it must be nearly supper-time, and he'll never stay to supper. And if he is there, we needn't undo it. Then, after supper, we could go round to our old man.'

I had no objection to offer to this, for I had quite forgotten to buy any food. I decided, however, to call at Willy's on the way round and purchase some suitable contributions to the meal. It was now nearly half-past seven. I moved for my oilskin, but Marney interrupted me, grinning.

'You shut it up,' he said. 'You know we haven't proved yet it *will* shut up.'

I chuckled.

'We'll soon do that,' I said, leaning over, and releasing the catch.

The netting at once grew slack, but the bows, instead of falling with their own weight, as they had done before the pot was netted, only moved about an inch. I put the weight of my hand on one of them. It moved, but not more than another inch. Then with a horrible feeling in the pit of my stomach, I pressed with all my strength at all three bows. The netting creaked, but the bows remained still almost completely erect, and refused to move farther.

11

We stared at the pot for a long time in silence. Then Marney remarked with an ominous quietness:

'It's a *very* queer thing. Won't it shut up any more than that?'

He put both his hands on top of the bows and pressed. There was a movement when he left go, but it was a springlike jerk to an even more erect position.

'It's a *very* queer thing,' he repeated. 'It worked all right before the net was put on. It's the net that's holding it. Damn it, the thing's not going to be much use if it won't shut up, *is* it?'

I did not need Marney to tell me that it was the net that resisted the collapsing operation; for most of its meshes seemed tighter in the semi-erect position than when the frame was rigid; and his second remark did not tend to relieve my acute dismay. I was seeing my dreams dissipate like the steam from a memorable train. I had a powerful wish that Marney would go, and leave me to face the bitterness of humiliation alone; but his next remark brought a gleam of hope.

'Damn it, the little pot worked all right. Why can't this one?'

I took the little pot from the cupboard. It was collapsed. I opened it and closed it again. It worked as easily as before. I looked with growing hope at the big pot. There was no essential difference between the two, I told myself, except that the bows of the small one were made of thin flexible wire. If one worked, surely the other must. I tried the big pot again, but produced no appreciable movement in the desired direction. I tried the small one. It collapsed instantly the erecting bar was released. And suddenly with complete dismay, I understood why. The bows of the big pot were themselves rigid. The bows of the small one 'gave' in the collapsing process, accommodating themselves to the increased strain of the net. A fullsize pot with bows of thin wire would be absurd. *My collapsing indestructible lobster pot was not a practical device.*

I felt myself going hot and cold. I thought of the telegram in my pocket, and of the letter which would reach me to-morrow; and I had a sudden impulse to put the new pot on the floor, stamp on it, and collapse it once and for all. But the intolerable tension of the moment was relieved by the sound of quick footsteps, followed by the sound of the latch.

'It's Amy,' Marney said a little nervously. 'It must be supper-time.'

I opened the door and Amy came in. She had a shawl over her head and looked extremely cross.

'Do you know what the time is?' she shouted at Marney. 'I've had the supper ready nearly half an hour, and now I've had to come out in the rain and fetch you. What on earth have you been doing all this time?'

Marney pointed to the pot, as he might have pointed, I thought, to the victim of a tragic accident he had discovered.

'We've got it netted,' he said, quietly, as though to suggest to Amy that she had stepped into the presence of the dead, 'and it won't shut up.'

Amy looked at the pot, but she did not seem to be deeply impressed.

'I don't see that's any reason for not coming for your supper. You've got plenty of time to play at making patent lobster pots between meal times, without causing all this bother.'

'There's no play about it,' Marney retorted with sudden indignation. 'That thing may be worth millions of pounds if it can be made to work like the first one did. I'd do without any supper altogether, if I could find out what's wrong with it. Aye, I'd starve for a week.'

'Well, you can starve by yourself then,' Amy answered, moving to the door. 'I've fried those three plaice, and Tom's been to the fish shop for some chips, and everything's ready. You can come back later, the two of you, if Tom stays on. . . . Now come on at once,' she added with a more generous persuasion. 'You'll not work at it any better for being hungry.'

I made a sign to Marney that he had better go, but for me the thought of sitting down to a meal with this weight on my mind was nauseating. They went. I locked the door behind them, and sat down at the table, in front of the two pots.

A drowning man will clutch at a straw. I searched for a straw desperately. I worked the little pot again, letting the bows down gradually, so as to make certain whether the wire did bend when the strain of the net increased. They did so, a matter of nearly threequarters of an inch, when the strain was at its greatest; but repeating the operation, I decided that the strain was produced, not by the main net, but by the spouts, which in the collapsing process were folded. I looked at the big pot. I discovered that it ceased its collapsing movement precisely when the folding of the spouts began. Would it work if the spouts were untied?

They were stretched by two double lengths of manilla to the opposite side of the pot. It took me an appreciable time to find their knots, so cunningly had Marney, in his desire for artistic effect, concealed them; and the knots themselves were so securely tied that I was obliged to cut them. I was glad that Marney was not watching me. His lovely spout became a shapeless heap of netting when I cut the second knot, but the æsthetic loss was a practical gain. The tension of the whole netting relaxed. Of their own account the bows dropped until they were brought up by the strain of the second spout. I did not trouble to hunt for the knots of this one. I slashed the fastenings with my knife, and once more the pot was a collapsible pot in a collapsed condition.

I had found my straw! But I saw at once that it was a straw, and nothing more substantial yet. I had proved that the pot would work without the spouts. The spouts, however, were indispensable, and while it was of no importance what happened to them when the pot was collapsed, it was essential that they should be stretched and rigid for fishing. I erected the pot again, bolted it, and tied up the spouts more or less as they had been before. It would not be practical to do this under fishing conditions, I reflected. But if the spouts could be raised and lowered automatically, then the problem would be solved.

I lit a fag, and concentrated on these two gracefully shaped, cunning cones of net. My own future, the prosperity of an industry, the happiness of thousands depended on my solving that problem. I smoked my fag until it burnt my lips; I lit another from it, and went on smoking fag after fag, oblivious to time, that my fire had gone out, that I was cold and hungry, and dizzy with tobacco fumes; and suddenly I was inspired. If, instead of attaching the spouts direct to the opposite side of the pot, I led the cords through loops to the bows, then as soon as the bows were unfastened, the cords would slacken, and the spouts would automatically fall. Rings would be better than loops, I thought quickly. The small rings (known technically as 'thimbles') which are used on sails to ease the friction of a running rope, would be admirable for this purpose; and there would certainly be some in the Lunn's warehouse. But as I got up, my eyes fell upon my fishing rod. This was fitted with half a dozen such rings, except that they were made of white porcelain, and secured to the rod in expensive gun metal mounts. They would be infinitely better than sail thimbles.

I hurried down to the washhouse for my pliers, the hack-saw and a file. The wind was still south-west, and it was still raining. I saw that the Brewster's cottage was in darkness as I came back.

It was not without a twinge of remorse that I laid destructive hands upon my fishing rod, for it was an old and trusty one, and had served me well in many an exciting fight. But Henry Lunn by this time would be in bed, and it might take me hours to find a set of sail thimbles in the warehouse. Too much hung on the issue of this experiment for me to gib at the sacrifice of my rod.

I ruthlessly removed four of the porcelain thimbles, and attached two of them to the sides of the pot at the point where the spout cords had been fastened. I increased the length of these cords, led them through the thimbles, and then strained them at right angles to the farthest end bow, and made them fast. The spout was now taut as it had been when Marney left it. I resisted the temptation to release the catch, and see if it would work. There was the second spout. I secured this in similar fashion, and then I stood back and lit another fag.

It was a tense moment. I had accepted Henry Lunn's condition of the usefulness of a collapsible pot, that it should open and shut as simply as an umbrella. My frame had certainly fulfilled this condition; but unless the whole thing fell when I released the catch, I knew that my frame was valueless. I threw my fag away and lit another. Then, as one takes a plunge into a cold bath, I put one hand on the catch and gave it a slight pressure. The bows fell on to the metal base with a clatter that made me jump.

There was no need for me to prove that it would open again; but I opened it. I let it fall again. I opened it and locked it. I put my watch on the table and timed each operation. I found that I could open and close it in less than ten seconds. I locked it again, and then stood back, confident that I had at last solved every problem.

But as I looked at it I was assailed by a new uneasiness. It was no longer the simple device that I had conceived, and that the blacksmith and Marney and I had made. The arrangement of thimbles and cords worked better than I had imagined. But the interior of the pot looked as complicated as the rigging of a sailing ship without the justification of masts and sails. Lines seemed to run everywhere. There seemed to be no clear piece of netting left. The graceful sweep of the spouts was completely masked and spoilt, and the whole thing was untidy and unbeautiful. I thought of dad and his patent easel and its elaborations; of his academy pictures into which he inevitably painted a flock of sheep, or a coble sail, destroying the beauty of space. My pot *looked* wrong. It looked wrong because it *was* wrong, unpractical, unseamanlike. I stepped towards it, slashed away the thimbles and the long cords, and tied the spouts back in their original positions, so that once more it was almost as Marney had made it, and beautiful.

Yet once more it was non-collapsible. I sat down,

staring at it, and went on smoking. My experiment, which had cost me my fishing rod, had at least proved something. The pot would work if the spouts were automatically lowered. My device failed only because it was too complicated. Could I achieve the same effect in a simple way? I began methodically to analyse the whole structure of the net, to determine the exact purpose of every one of Marney's knots. The intense concentration aggravated the effect of the tobacco, however. I was soon seeing knots where there were no knots; and the meshes dazzled me like water ripples in the sun. I thought I had better light my fire and make some tea.

But I had no sooner got the kettle on than a fresh idea came to me. I had watched Marney very closely when he had put the netting on. The spouts were secured to the bows quite independently of the 'roof' and doors. The latter I had proved grew slack immediately the catch was released. Would it be possible to attach the entrances of the spouts direct to them, so that when they slackened, the spouts would slacken, too?

I was glad again that Marney was not with me to witness the ruthless spoilation of his handiwork this new experiment entailed. I cut away the rows of beautifully formed clove hitches that held one of the spouts to the base and legs of the bows. I cut the attachments of the adjacent netting. The effect was appalling for each cut gave me two loose ends, which threatened to 'run,' at the slightest strain, like a ladder in a silk stocking. I did not know how to 'net' the various sections together again. I simply tied them, mesh to mesh, with a separate piece of twine, which added two more untidy ends to every pair of meshes joined. I was no longer concerned with æsthetic effects, however. If the thing worked it would be worth having an entirely new net, and I could trust Marney to make the necessary modifications. Once more I refrained from trying it with the first half done. I cut the other spout adrift and patched it up; and then fortifying myself for another plunge with another fag, I unfastened the catch. *The pot collapsed perfectly.*

My fire had gone out. I lit it again. I found some eggs in the pantry. I boiled them and made tea. I erected the pot and put it in the middle of the table and set my meal in front of it, so that I could look at it while I fed. It looked patched, untidy. It bristled with twine ends. But these meant no more to me than the first experimental lines of a drawing, that would be rubbed out when the permanent lines were pencilled in. It looked right, as simple and efficient and seamanlike as an anchor. I took out my telegram again and read it through; and I allowed my mind to wander pleasantly into the future, when factories would be turning out my pots by the thousand, and the moribund fishing villages and ports of the British coasts would be throbbing with new life and prosperity. A new boat would be specially built for the Lunns, I thought. They would be given permanent employment by whatever organization came into being for the manufacture and sale of the pots and the development of the lobster fishing industry. There would be the conservatism of many of the older fishermen to overcome. The Fosdycks for example, who obstinately refused to have anything to do with motors, would take some persuading that their own gear was now completely obsolete. The best argument was practical demonstration. The Lunns would do this. Using my pots they would catch more lobsters, in less time, and without loss of gear. They would be employed, too, in searching for the distant and hitherto unexploited grounds which Henry Lunn had mentioned. For them at least it would mean the end of their present precarious way of living.

For myself, I thought, I asked nothing beyond the wherewithal to pay my debts, and pay my way, and have someone to do my cooking and washing-up. I craved neither for wealth nor power, for both had their obligations and worries. I could not imagine anything more agreeable than to join the Lunns in a staunch, well-found deep-sea boat, demonstrating to the inshore fishermen of the British coasts, exploring new fishing-grounds, studying the feeding and migratory habits of the lobster and other fish; perhaps in time venturing to still more distant waters in search of our living treasure.

I had finished my meal. The south-west wind was still blowing outside my cottage. I could hear the rain, and suddenly I heard the rumble of coble wheels. It was nearly six o'clock. I pulled up the corner of my blind and saw that it was still completely dark. Another raid beginning! I collapsed my lobster pot, and the noise it made was like the rattle of a rifle bolt. I pulled my sea-boots on, and got into my oilskins, and having locked both doors behind me, I stumbled down the dark, rain-swept lane towards the Dock.

BOO K TWO

1

IT was shortly after dark, on a calm night in February, that I stole quietly from my cottage past the Brewsters' towards the Green, and the gas-house route to the Lunns' warehouse. I carried my pot in a special canvas bag that Marney had made for me; and I moved with haste, for I was leaving Bramblewick on an important mission by the seven o'clock train.

After months of exasperating delay, things at last were moving. Mr. X as I had previously known, was an extremely busy man, a director of several important companies, and actively connected with certain international organizations, which frequently made it necessary for him to travel abroad. He had also, I gathered, a business man's cautiousness. He had assisted me financially, and with expert advice, in the procuring of a provisional patent; but he had warned me that the placing of an invention on the market was a slow and difficult process. Our best way of doing this was either to form a private company, or to work on a profit-sharing basis, with some established manufacturer; and in either case I must submit some very substantial evidence as to the commercial value of my invention. He had proposed that my model should be shown in confidence to the experts of the Ministry of Agriculture and Fisheries. I had been honoured by a visit from the District Inspector of Fisheries (a retired naval officer), who obviously had been deeply impressed by the pot, and by Henry Lunn's testimony as to its usefulness. But his report had been a cautiously worded one. He considered that the invention had great possibilities but that it was impossible to come to a definite conclusion until it was tested under actual fishing conditions. He advised that we should have a number of them manufactured, and that the Lunns should try them against their own pots during the forthcoming season, when another official examination might be made.

Unfortunately Mr. X had left England before this report had reached him. It was not until this morning that I had received a letter to say that he considered the report highly satisfactory, and that I should proceed to have the pots made at once. A cheque to cover their cost and my travelling expenses was enclosed. He agreed with a suggestion I had made that I should call on various manufacturers in the Midland industrial area, and obtain as many estimates as possible for the ultimate cost of manufacture; and he made the additional suggestion that if I found a firm eager to take the thing up on a profit-sharing basis, I should intimate that the matter might be discussed in detail at an early date.

The morning's post had brought also a letter from a well-known manufacturer in Birmingham, to whom I had been given a written introduction by a mutual friend. This gentleman, Mr. N, whose firm produced a patented metal device with an annual sale of millions, said that he would be very pleased to have details of my invention, and that he would be glad to give me any advice or assistance within his power. I had decided that I would call on him to-morrow; and I had wired him to this effect.

The pot was provisionally patented; which meant that it was legally protected from infringement for a period of nine months, by which time a complete patent must be filed. But although, according to Marney, various rumours were current in the village about my activities, and that it was common knowledge that I had invented 'summat,' no one except the Lunns had seen the pot, and there were several reasons why its secret should not be divulged at present. Collapsed, and in its canvas case, it looked as though it might be a framed picture or some article of furniture I was carrying; and my route was deliberately chosen so that I should not meet anyone who might connect it with my visit to the Lunns. I wished to see them to say good-bye, and to exhibit the pot for the last time for criticism and approval.

It was after tea-time, and I knew that all three would be in the warehouse; for, if the weather permitted, they were going to take their pots to sea, for the first time, to-morrow. There was a large stack of pots just outside the door, and opening the door I saw that this was a mere overflow, for apart from a small area in front of the fire, all the space of the room was filled with pots and immense coils of tarry rope. Here, by the fire, Henry and

John and Marney were engaged attaching the short lengths of rope which they called 'strops' to individual pots, the final operation which made them ready for fishing.

I had already told them of my plans. Marney greeted me ironically.

'God, I wish I was all dolled up, and going off on my holidays.'

'Aye,' said John with a grin. 'I do. It's a damned fine spot is Birmingham. I was once there on a choir trip. There's a Woolworth's six times bigger than the one at Burnharhour.'

'Is that the pot you've got there in that bag?' Henry put in, more practically. 'You'd hardly think you could get a full-size lobster pot into a thing like that. Take it out and let's have a look at it.'

'Aye. But we'll have the door bolted, first,' said Marney.

He got up and bolted it. I took the pot from the case, and laid it on a fish box, near the fire and clear of the tarry rope. I opened it; and although each of the Lunns had already performed this operation many times for himself, there was a united expression of admiration, in which I found it hard not to join.

Except in one important detail, the pot was practically as I had completed it on that memorable night. The netting was of course new; yet my plan of making the spouts and roof and doors in one piece had offered no serious problem to Marney; and it was the identical design without my disfiguring knots. The important alteration was in the locking device. The original catch had worked perfectly when the netting was dry. When wetted, however, manilla shrinks to an extraordinary degree, and I had found that after the pot had been immersed in my rain water cistern for a few minutes, it was impossible to move the catch the slight fraction of an inch necessary to free it from its socket; and that it was equally impossible to force the catch into the socket again from the collapsed condition. My new device was a catch consisting of a handle, and double metal claws, hinged to the end of the erecting bar. When the pot was almost erect, the claws were engaged on the middle bow, affording a powerful leverage against the tension of the net. The whole catch was swung over, and at the moment of maximum tension it fell on to the coupling bar, and locked the pot securely. To unlock it again one had only to lift the catch, an operation as quick and simple as the closing of an umbrella.

I was particularly proud of this catch. I had sawed and filed the claws from a piece of the baby carriage. The handle was made from an unnecessary gas bracket I had found in the cottage, and part of an old bicycle pedal, and there were several other components. True that it was not so simple and neat as the catch it had replaced; but it was remarkably efficient; and when manufactured the whole thing would be stamped or cast in a single piece.

The Lunns were still gaping at the pot in admiration. I explained that I was showing it to them for the last time and that I wished them to make sure that they had no fault to find with it; and that they wished me to have the pots for the final official test made exactly to its plan.

'I don't see any fault in it,' Henry said promptly. 'In

my opinion it's just right for what it's for. And I don't care who you show it to, landsmen or fishermen, they'd have to say the same thing, if they speak the truth. It's a real champion idea.'

'I wish we were taking ninety of them instead of ninety of ours to sea to-morrow,' said Marney. 'It wouldn't matter then whether it was fine weather or not.'

'Aye,' Henry agreed. 'We'll have the coble piled up like a hay-cart, and even then we'll have to make two trips of it.'

'God,' said John. 'It makes our pots look clumsy affairs, doesn't it? It's like looking at an old coal barge, and then at a yacht. Look how fine and regular those bows are compared with ours!'

I glanced from my own pot to one of the hazel pots close by, and J felt that the comparison was just; and my faith was not shaken when Marney remarked thoughtfully:

'Aye. It looks champion, and no mistake. The only fault I can see in it is the side sticks. I know it's strong enough without them; that it wouldn't shut up if you had them. But I still think ours look better along the sides.'

'They may *look* better, but they're *not* better,' Henry championed sharply. 'That pot's right, I tell you. And all I wish is that we were starting off with them, tomorrow, instead of with ours.'

'We'd certainly show the Fosdycks a thing or two,' said John.

'We'd show them all a thing or two,' said Marney quite enthusiastic again, 'We'd catch more lobsters than those big Burnharbour boats and them with twice as

155

many pots. It's my opinion this pot will *fish* better, too. It's finer gear. Finer the gear more fish you'll get in any sort of fishing. Look what that little pot did, first time it was set!'

I was glad that Marney had mentioned this point of fishing; for after our first scare of discovery with the small model, I had not dared to risk the big model on the scaur ends, and there had been no opportunity for giving it a real test in deep water.

There was a silence; and I remembered that I had still some packing to do before I left for the station. I laid my hand on the catch, and in the manner of a chairman putting a motion to a meeting, said:

'Then you're all satisfied?'

'Aye,' Marney and John said together.

'Aye,' Henry repeated. 'The thing's right. It's right for us, and it will be right for every fisherman so long as it doesn't cost too much brass. Don't trouble about the net. Most fishermen will want to make that for themselves. The frame's the important thing. If you make it so that you can sell it under five bob, I tell you you'll sell thousands. There'll not be another hazel pot made, to be smashed up the first bit of bad weather. But it mustn't cost more than five bob.'

I was still uncertain as to the cost of manufacture. But I was confident that it would be considerably less than this figure. The smith had charged me two shillings for making the bows and the bars and my original catch. The base, even when hand-made, could not cost more than another two, and the new catch should not cost more than twopence. The original model of the Ford car had cost more to make than the most luxurious Rolls Royce. Mass production had brought it within the means of the relatively poor. There were articles in Woolworth's which, singly, would cost at least a pound to make. Mass production had brought their selling price to pence. And my pot was pre-eminently suited for mass production. Every part of it would be stamped, or cast by the thousand; every one so made would progressively reduce the ultimate cost of the unit.

I collapsed the pot and slipped it into its case. The Lunns went on with their job. For a moment I watched them, and the roughly made, clumsy pots they were handling; and I experienced a sudden and peculiar misgiving, a distrust of my own invention that was to replace the gear which had served so many generations of fishers. I wished suddenly that I knew how to make a hazel pot; and how to form the special knots in the 'strops' that were being bent on to them. And I wished that I was not catching the night train to Birmingham, but instead joining the Lunns at daybreak on the first expedition of the lobster season. But my confidence as quickly returned; and I picked up the case.

'Well, so long everybody,' I said. 'I hope it's a fine morning for you and that you do well.'

Henry looked up from his task and smiled.

'Aye. We shan't need to do very well, to do better than we've done with cod. And I hope you have good luck with that gentleman you're going to see, and that you'll soon be back with those shut-up pots. We'll soon show the Fisheries chap what we can do with them.'

'You'll call on Amy on your way to the station, won't

you?' said Marney. 'I'd come up with you if we hadn't all this gear to fettle. Tell her to keep supper hot for me, if I'm late, and not to come bothering over here. Good luck!'

'Good luck!' said John; and he called after me as I reached the door: 'If you have any time to spare in Birmingham and you happen to notice any music shops, you might pop in and ask them for their price list of brass instruments. Ask them if you get any reduction when you buy everything for a band at one go—drum included!'

2

A record frost which was to break the meteorological records of many years in its widespread intensity, descended on the British Isles during that night.

In the country a hard, seasonable frost is exciting. There is something dramatic in visible ice, in the changed aspect of familiar streams and ponds; in the sight of nipped tree buds and stricken plants, in the mute terror of starving birds, in the fierce stillness that reigns over frozen fields and woodlands. One is aware that an invisible force more powerful than the force of great storms is at work upon the face of nature. The still air seems charged with the rays of a cosmic bombardment, ruthlessly blasting the forward or unwary growth of plant and animal life, destroying the weak and unfit, and unwise, increasing by a sudden thousandfold the hazards of the struggle for existence.

Yet in a city, and particularly in a city like Birmingham, which to a stranger appears to possess no parks or trees or visible water, the only evidences of frost are a discomforting chill in the smoke-polluted air, the steaming breath of wretched horses, policemen on point duty stamping their feet, thick coated and begloved tram drivers, clapping their hands together, and a look of resigned suffering on the faces of the street population.

The extensive works of Mr. N lay some two miles east of the business section of the city, on one of the direct tram routes; but I allowed myself the luxury of a taxi-cab. I had been told by my friend that I should like Mr. N. He was Yorkshire born, and a 'self-made' man who had started at the very foot of the ladder, but was completely unspoilt by success. He was a specialist in mass production. I could rely absolutely, on his judgment respecting my invention and its commercial possibilities, and I could count myself very fortunate if I persuaded him to take a practical interest in it, for he had an uncanny instinct for knowing what would sell, and how to sell it.

My first impressions of that interview certainly were agreeable. I was ushered into a large office that was more like a room in a house; warmed by a splendid fire; and Mr. N himself rose from behind a desk, came forward and shook my hand as though I had been an old friend. He was middle-aged, of sturdy build, clean shaven with clear blue eyes, and slightly greying hair, and with just a suspicion of 'Yorkshire' in his way of speaking. But what impressed me most was his heartiness, his good spirits, his energy. His manners were charming. He swung two chairs round to the fire, made me sit down and offered me a cigar. He did not sit down himself, however, and he did not smoke. He stood with his back to the fire, rubbing his hands together, shifting his balance from foot to foot, while he spoke rapidly and breezily of our mutual friend, about the frost, about Bramblewick (which he had once visited), about the fishermen of the coast, whom he understood were having a very bad time of it. Then, with a sudden glance at my case, he said:

'Well, I was very interested to hear about this new lobster pot of yours. I don't know much about fishing, I'll confess, but I'm always interested in anything that's new. Have you got it in that bag?'

I had carefully rehearsed the demonstration of my pot. A fisherman would not need to be told the advantages of its strength and collapsibility. But to impress a landsman it was necessary to prepare his mind by describing briefly the economic disadvantages of the old type of gear. There was no need for details. The main point was that the old type of pot was easily destroyed, that it handicapped the fishermen by its bulk and weight. A pot whose frame was made of iron or steel, that could when not in use be folded so as to occupy one-sixth of its erect space would obviously solve this economic problem.

To this Mr. N listened with quiet interest, and he looked with evident eagerness at the case when I had done. He moved over to his desk and cleared a space for me. I took the pot from the case, and laid it there. It was collapsed. The net was slack, completely shapeless: as unsuggestive of its rigid form as the deflated envelope of a balloon. The bows were hidden under the net. The beautifully shaped spouts were indistinguishable from the rest of the net.

I laid my hand on the pot.

'This,' I said, 'is the thing I have invented, closed. It lies flat, and packs snugly. It is less than half the weight of the ordinary pot.'

'Yes!' Mr. N said quickly.

I took hold of the erecting bar, opened the pot, pushed the catch over, and stood back like a conjurer who has produced a live goose from a silk hat.

'And this is all that has to be done to make it ready for fishing.'

I heard Mr. N give an unmistakable gasp of astonishment. For a full minute he looked at it in silence. Then he remarked slowly:

'Now that's clever. That's very very clever!'

And he was looking at it now with eagle eyes.

'Angle iron, eh?' he went on. 'That's going to be strong and no mistake, and particularly with those ribs across. And the bottom is all wood in the old sort of pot, and those hoops just bent hazels? I should say that it would take a very rough sea to smash up that bottom. . . . And the lobsters go in by those two funnels? Where does the bait go? How do you get the lobsters out?'

I demonstrated the doors, and put my handkerchief in the bait string. I ignored my own invention for the time being, and speaking as it were for the Lunns, and the generations of fishers who had evolved that cunning and lovely contraption, I explained the whole netting. Until now, I said, the type of pot used by the Lunns had proved itself superior to any other type. All that I claimed for my invention was that I had adapted their net to my special frame.

'And have you proved that yours will catch lobsters as well as theirs?' Mr. N demanded.

'I have proved that it will at least fish as well,' I said modestly; and, remembering Marney's remark, I added, 'But according to the Lunns, it will fish even better, for it's finer gear. Any fisherman or angler knows that fine gear is more deadly than coarse.'

There was another short silence; then Mr. N remarked with a sudden peculiar curtness:

'I don't know anything about fishing or angling. I've always thought that a man who can sit for hours on a wet bank or a draughty pier, waiting and waiting for a fish to bite must be a fool. But it looks to me as though you'd got something here that might have some money in it, if it's handled properly. I'd want to know a lot more about it before *I* handled it, of course. But if what you and your fishermen say is right, it seems that no fisherman will be able to afford *not* to use this pot. It would be like a stage coach trying to compete with a motor car. Did you say that you'd taken out a provisional patent?'

I took from my pocket the official receipt for my patent claim, and put it in Mr. N's hand. He glanced at it, and then said abruptly:

'Well now, what do you want to do about it? Do you want to sell the patent outright and be finished with it, or do you want to work it on a royalty basis, so much per cent on sales?'

I was prepared to find Mr. N impressed. But this, I thought was verging on a tentative offer, and I trod warily. I explained my position with Mr. X and the Ministry of Agriculture and Fisheries; that the chief object of my visit was to obtain expert advice with regard to the purely manufacturing side; to find out approximately what the mass production cost would be, and to have a batch of twenty pots made for the final official test. But, I added that I was anxious to secure the practical co-operation of an established manufacturer; and that this question might be gone into when the test, the result of which was a foregone conclusion, was completed.

'Yes,' Mr. N remarked. 'We'd want to see the thing properly tested, of course; and a favourable Government report would be very valuable when it came to selling. And we'd want a close idea of what it would cost, too, and what it would sell for. . . . Well, let's see roughly what it would cost to make apart from the net, which you say the men would want to make for themselves.'

He examined the framework intently.

'What's its weight?' he remarked.

I had carefully measured the weight against one of the Lunns' ballasted pots. Mine, without the net, weighed eighteen pounds. Mr. N leaned over the desk and made some calculations on a piece of paper. I waited with perfect confidence, thinking of the smith who had made all but the base of the original pot for two shillings. Mr. N turned again to the pot, and seemed to be checking his calculations. Then he remarked:

'Well, I think I can tell you within a few pence, what

163

it's going to cost to make in large quantities. Of course, as you know, the more you make the less the cost, down to a reasonable figure. You've still got your raw material, remember. But before I tell you, I'd like to know your idea of what it will sell for. Fishermen aren't millionaires, are they? They'd want it pretty cheap.'

'Yes,' I answered. 'The cheaper the better. It mustn't cost them much more than their present gear, of course. I thought about five shillings.'

There was a silence; an ominous silence. I was aware that Mr. N was looking at me with an astonished smile.

'Five shillings!' he echoed suddenly. 'Why, it would cost nearly twice that to make it and galvanize it! Without allowing a farthing for selling costs, for carriage, for retailer's commission, and overheads. You couldn't sell a thing like that under twenty-five shillings, to make it pay!'

I said nothing. I had the sensation of being struck a violent blow in the stomach.

'Five shillings!' Mr. N repeated. 'Your material would cost you two and threepence to start with. You might get a country blacksmith to make you one or two out of scrap like this one is made; but you couldn't use scrap for making them in thousands. You have to pay twopence a pound for angle iron, and about as much for what the other parts are made of. Galvanizing would cost at least threepence a pound. There's another four-and-six. You couldn't have that bottom frame cast unless you had it three times as thick. It would be too brittle. That bottom would have to be nearly all hand-made, unless you had it stamped, and the machinery for stamping a thing like that would cost you thousands of pounds. . . . Do you really think that the fishermen wouldn't be able to pay more than five shillings for something that's going to give him such a big pull over his old type of gear? A motor boat costs more than a sailing boat, doesn't it, but the fishermen now have to use motor boats if they're going to make a living.'

It was a deadly comparison, for I was already thinking of the Fosdycks, who despite that their savings would allow them to do so, had obstinately refused to install a motor in their coble. It would be a difficult enough task to persuade them to use patent pots even if they cost less than their own. To expect them or even modern minded fishers like the Lunns to pay five times as much was unthinkable.

I expressed this opinion to Mr. N in definite terms. Six shillings was the maximum figure we could ever hope to get from the pot. He did not glance at the pot again. He moved across to the fire, turned and spoke with a kindliness, with a fatherliness in his voice that completed my dismay.

'Well, I'm sorry, but it's no use to me. It's a pity. You've got a very clever thing there, very clever indeed, and I can see that it would be a godsend to those poor fishermen. But you've got to look at it from a practical point of view. Before a manufacturer could start making a thing like that he'd have to lay down a lot of money. He'd want his world patents for one thing. That might cost him anything up to a thousand pounds when all the lawyers' fees were paid. He'd want special tools. I've got tools in my shops that have cost me five hundred pounds apiece, and that doesn't include the machines for using them. There's raw material, there's labour at trade union rates, there's selling costs, advertising, travellers, there's retailer's commission, carriage, royalty to the inventor, overheads, bad debts, and there's his own profit and what's to go to his shareholders, all to come out of the selling price. That's what you inventor's don't realize! A thing can be so clever that it takes your breath away with admiration, but unless its production cost is at least four hundred per cent less than its selling price, no manufacturer is going to risk his money on it. Personally, there's nothing I dislike more than turning away an idea that I can see is clever and original. And there's scarcely a day that I haven't got to do it. I get people coming to see me with things they've spent years of hard work and study on; yes, and very often every farthing they've possessed, too. They've got something clever and original, but it's not a practical manufacturing proposition. I've known a man burst into tears when I've told him the unpleasant truth.'

Tears at that moment could not have expressed the despair in my own heart. I listened mechanically as Mr. N went on.

'Of course I'm not criticizing the idea itself. I'm only looking at it from a manufacturer's point of view. I should think if you studied the thing out, you might simplify it, and reduce the cost considerably. You might substitute wood for metal in some of the parts. Wood can't be so useless for the job if the fishermen have been using it for so many generations. It's cheap, and it hasn't got to be galvanized, remember. You might simplify that catch. It's clever, but it's expensive. A little bolt might do just as well. But anyway, from what you've told me, I'm certain it's not a thing for me to handle, or any other manufacturer. The only thing I can suggest is that you have your twenty made and tested by the Government; and then if they prove a very great success, get hold of some very wealthy man who would risk getting say a thousand of them made, and loaning them to the fishermen on a profit-sharing basis. There ought to be money in that. The fishermen would be paying you several times over for what the pot cost, and the thing would still be yours. And you'd have no selling costs at all.'

It was a cunning suggestion. Modified so as to preclude the risk of the fishermen being exploited, it contained the seed for hope. After all, I had not come to Mr. N expecting him to make an immediate proposal to take up my invention. My main object was to get the pots made. I asked Mr. N if he would undertake their manufacture. My spirits which were beginning to rise, sank again when he replied rather quickly that it would not be possible at present as his works were at full pressure. He would, however, give me the names of several firms who most likely would be glad to do the work, and he quickly jotted these down on a piece of paper, and handed it to me. I saw that the interview was ended. I packed the pot, and thanked Mr. N for his kindness in giving me so much of his time. There was the same warmth in his good wishes to me as there had been in his first reception, yet the slight glow of it seemed to vanish immediately I stepped out into the street, and I experienced the physical shock of that record frost, which in Mr. N's pleasantly heated office I had forgotten.

It was a narrow gloomy street, with the works of my late host making a monotonous wall on one side of it; and the other side consisting, as far as one could see through the murky atmosphere, of other factories and warehouses. It was filled with the grind and clatter of electric trams and heavy motor lorries, and from the factories came a steady muffled roar that reminded me of the surf at Bramblewick. I wished that I was back there, in Marney's cottage, in front of a big fire, with the kettle boiling for tea. I wished even for my own cottage. I wanted to think, to solve the urgent problem of what I was to do next.

I walked along the street, not knowing whether I was going east or west. I followed the tram lines. I was bewildered by all that had transpired in my interview. Ringing in my ears was that fatal phrase, 'twentyfive shillings'. It was like a death sentence on all my dreams. The normal equipment of pots for a small boat was ninety. That would mean an outlay of at least a hundred pounds. What fisherman could find that capital, even if he could be persuaded that it would be a sound investment. If Mr. N was right in his estimate of costs, then clearly the thing was a failure. Had I not best give it up altogether, go back to Bramblewick and make another effort to write again?

The thought was revolting. To do that would be to acknowledge a humiliating defeat. Could I sit writing with the sound of the sea mocking me? Could I face 'Bramblewick', and the mocking smiles of the Fosdycks, and Reub Brewster and Jane, and Willy (from whom I would be obliged to accept a further financial accommodation)? True, that only the Lunns would know the nature of my defeat, but 'Bramblewick' would smell it as a fly smells bad meat.

No, I thought. By God, no! I must have my pots made, and take them back with me. Whether they were to be a commercial success or not, I would prove their practical worth in the sea, and if it were not possible to manufacture them and sell them to the fishermen at a reasonable price, then some other means of making them available must be considered. The plan suggested by Mr. N had possibilities. Perhaps Mr. X himself might be persuaded to put down the necessary capital, if the official test proved highly favourable.

I stopped and felt in my pocket for the list of firms. I remembered that I had left it on Mr. N's desk when I was packing up the pot. But the thought of going back was not agreeable. On every side of me were factories. The freezing air stank with the fumes of furnaces and burning metal. Almost opposite me, where I had stopped, was a grimy building with the name of a firm and under it:

LIGHT STEEL STAMPINGS, FRAMES, BUCKETS, CANS, HOOPS, ETC.

There was a door labelled OFFICE. I stepped inside and was accosted by an alert-looking clerk. I decided that I would be discreet as to the exact nature of what I wanted. I informed the youth that I was an inventor and that I wished to obtain a rough estimate for making certain parts of an apparatus in mass quantities, and that I would like to see somebody who would be able to give me such an estimate.

The clerk was impressed. There was a counter between us. He raised a section of it, and moved to let me to pass through, and he led me through the office to a covered passage terminating in another door. This he opened. A dull roar that had been manifest in the office suddenly became a devilish din. The clerk signed to me to wait, and left me, just inside the threshold of a large workshop, that was filled with clanging, thumping, roaring machines. They were stamping machines. Each was attended by a bare-armed, bare-headed, aproned woman. The noise was so intense that it actually hurt ones ears, like heavy gun-fire. It would have been impossible to have heard the sound of human speech. The women at the machines indeed seemed like deaf mutes. Their faces, in the glare of the electric lamps which hung above them, eclipsing the feeble windowed glimmer of day, were pale and expressionless. A pile of circular metal blanks lay on a tray by the side of each machine. A hand jerked out to the pile like a mechanical claw. A blank was seized and slipped between the machine's gaping jaws, the upper jaw thumped savagely down. The metal yelped like a hurt animal. The jaw rose up, and the shaped utensil, a metal cup, was ejected on to a travelling belt, while another blank was slipped between the jaws.

Dazed by the noise, bewildered by the intricate movements of innumerable levers, of spinning pulleys and belts and flashing wheels, I felt that I had been transported into a nightmare world. I felt that the only living things in the room were the machines. They were alive. They breathed and moved, and their noises were coherent. They had strength and knowledge and purpose and fertility. There was rhythm and beauty in their lean moving pistons which glistened with oily sweat like the limbs of a straining athlete. But the women who served them were like corpses partly revived by some drug which kept their tissue fresh and gave them the power to stand erect and move their hands; yet left them without the power of conscious thought, or speech or hearing; insensible to pain, incapable of emotion. It was at once horrifying and fascinating.

Here was mass production! This, I had long ago conceived was how my pot should be made. The cups and other articles spat out by each machine on to the travelling belt, were the exact reverse of the moulds or tools that stamped and shaped them. Substitute for these moulds, moulds of my bows and bars and the locking catch, and these very machines might be stamping out the components of my pot; and a heavier machine might stamp out the complete bottom, holes included, in a single operation. These would be ejected similarly on to a travelling belt which would transport them to the assembly room. The whole thing could be made in a matter of minutes!

I began to feel hopeful again. The clerk returned. He signed to me to follow him down an aisle between the machines out into a courtyard into another quieter room in which the products of the stamping shop were being sorted in vast piles and finally led me to an office marked, WORKS MANAGER, and introduced me to the manager himself.

This gentleman, who was dressed in black, was tall, lean, dark, saturnine, and looked like the headmaster of a school. He had none of Mr. N's breezy geniality. He did not ask me to sit down, and he did not invite me to smoke. He glanced up from some writing he was doing, and in a quiet, almost apathetic voice asked me what he could do for me. He listened in silence while I told him that I was an inventor of a device, which I believed would revolutionize a certain branch of the fishing industry. It was made principally of light iron or steel which would be galvanized. I anticipated that I should want it made ultimately in very large quantities, in batches say of two thousand up to a hundred thousand; but that at present I was concerned only with having about a score to complete a Government test. I would like an estimate for the immediate manufacture of this experimental batch and for the larger quantities. Of course, I added quickly, the placing of the larger order would depend upon the satisfactory and reasonable execution of the smaller one. Did his firm do work of this description?

He replied without the slightest change of the gloomy expression of his face that his firm was always ready to undertake work within the capacity of its equipment, and at reasonable prices. If I would give him exact details of the apparatus he could tell me at once if it could be done, and give an approximate quotation. I said nothing. I took out the pot and put it on his desk. I erected it. The very act of doing so increased my confidence. Never had

I erected it so quickly; never, I thought, had the whole apparatus looked so efficient, so impressive. I stood back, watching the manager's face; but it did not change its expression. I waited for his comment, for at least some evidence of curiosity and surprise. He continued to look at it in apathetic silence as though collapsing lobster pots were as familiar a sight to him as the mass products of his firm's machines. I felt it imperative that one of us should speak, and I said:

'It's a new kind of lobster pot. The chief point about it is that it collapses.'

'Oh yes?' he commented listlessly.

'The ordinary ones are, of course, rigid,' I went on. And their frames are made of wood.'

'I see,' the manager remarked.

'It's the frame only that I want making.'

'I see,' he repeated. 'We couldn't make the string part, naturally.'

My spirits were rapidly sinking again. I waited, at a loss as to what to say next. But after a moment's silence the manager himself directed the conversation.

'You want an estimate for making twenty frames exactly like that and galvanized? And an estimate say for two thousand?'

'And for ten thousand, and a hundred thousand,' I said impressively. 'The whole idea of the thing is mass production.'

Like Mr. N, but with a complete lack of his enthusiasm, he examined the frame, measured it with a ruler, and made some calculations on paper. Then, in the same quiet, apathetic voice, he remarked:

'Well, it's impossible to give an exact quotation, until we've had a careful drawing of it made and every detail of cost calculated. We could not, of course, have stamping tools made until we got a definite large order, with the usual guarantee. We should have to make your twenty by hand. I should say roughly that they would cost you two pounds: and, of course, there would be packing and carriage.'

I gasped. For one moment I thought he meant two pounds for making the twenty pots. For one moment I imagined all my difficulties solved, and my dream a thrilling possibility again. The next moment, however, I realized that the figure he quoted was the price for a single pot, for he continued in his gloomy voice:

'I'm afraid we should require a deposit of at least half the value of the order before we put the job in hand, unless you could give us satisfactory references. That will be twenty pounds. Of course there would be considerable reduction with a larger order. We might get it down to twenty shillings, even fifteen shillings for quantities over four thousand. But two pounds would be the lowest price for the small batch. Do you want me to put it in hand at once?'

I replied that I would have to think the matter over first. He answered listlessly:

'Very well.' And he went on with his writing until I had packed the pot, when he obliged me with the information that I could reach the street direct if I turned to my right from his office; and he gloomily bade me good day.

I stopped irresolutely at the street door, dejected and

bewildered. The street was a tributary of the main street where the trams were running. There were factories on one side of it, and some dilapidated brick cottages, and a pub with a brightly-coloured glazed brick front on the other. Half way down to my right, away from the main street, a shabby hearse with a pair of miserable horses was drawn up at the open door of one of the cottages whose upper windows were smashed and stuffed with sacking and cardboard. A group of poverty-stricken women and children stood on the paving close by; and two old men and a sickly looking youth with a fag in his mouth, and his hands in his trousers pockets, stood shivering but interested, with their backs against the pub wall. The frost was becoming more intense. The smoke from the factory chimneys could find no outlet through the low pall of freezing mist, and it oozed like a liquor down the roofs, thickening the air with filthy fumes. A man in a bowler hat and a dark overcoat, carrying a wreath of startling white lilies, emerged from the cottage, slammed open the door of the hearse and put the wreath inside. One of the horses shook its harness intelligently, and the other woke from its cold stupor and neighed. I caught the gleam of varnished oak and brass in the cottage door, and in that moment I decided I had done with my patent lobster pot for ever. There was something infernal in all this: in the stenching sulphurous smoke, in these grimy walls behind which the machines were alive and the people were dead. I wanted to see the sky again, and feel a wind, and hear the roar of the sea, the screaming of gulls; I wanted to assure myself that there was a life where men lived, and were masters of their boats, of their gear, of their destinies. Never in my life had I longed for Bramblewick as I did at that moment. I thought of the Lunns, out with their pots for the first time, indifferent to the cold and the weather provided that it left the Landing Bar open to them, possessed by the fever of a new season's venture. I thought of them returning to the Landing, hauling their cobles up to the Dock, of the meals and the dry clothes that waited them. Their life was hard, ill-paid in cash, yet by God, it *was* a life. Their pots were not so good as mine, but they served; and in the very labour of making them, in the cutting of hazels in the autumn coloured woods, in the gathering of driftwood from the shore for their bottoms, in the joinery and netting by the light of the warehouse lantern was the stuff of life itself. I would give up my idea for a mass-production lobster pot. I would return to Bramblewick to-night, tell the Lunns that the thing was no good, and at daybreak to-morrow I'd go to sea with them for their first haul.

The funeral was heading away from the main street. I turned to my left and ran for a tram that had just stopped. It was labelled STATION.

3

I did not return to Bramblewick that night, however. I muddled my trains, and arrived about seven o'clock at Leeds with an hour to wait for a train to York, and it was too late to make a connection with the coastline service home.

An English provincial main line station is a comfortless place on a winter's night, and this was the coldest night in recorded British meteorological history. The average male and solitary wayfarer, finding himself confronted by such a wait, would have betaken himself to the station buffet and fortified himself with whisky. But I knew that with myself alcohol served only to accentuate a given state of mind, to brighten a happy mood, to make more sombre a sombre one. And my mood was immeasurably sombre.

There had been ample time in my long slow journey from Birmingham to react again from the violent reaction which had followed my interview with the works manager. For most of the way I had been alone, and I had unpacked the pot, laid it on the compartment seat and opened it. The immediate effect was heartening. The thing thrilled me with its beauty, with its simple efficiency, as much as it had ever done. I would be a fool, I thought, to abandon it just because two men had condemned it. Every inventor one had heard of had gone through a similar experience to mine. Some of the cleverest and most valuable inventions had been condemned by people just as competent as Mr. N, and the inventors had persisted in the face of all manner of hardships and disappointments and discouragements, until success came. And Mr. N had at least agreed that the pot was efficient, that it would fulfil the claims I made for it. He had condemned it only because of its cost. *Was* that five shillings of Henry Lunn the maximum the fisherman could afford for something which would give him such enormous advantages? Could the thing be simplified, as Mr. N suggested, so that its cost might be reduced? Galvanizing was a cost that I had completely underrated. But galvanizing or some other method of rust prevention was the very condition of using iron or steel in salt water. Rust was the most insidious weapon in the armament of the sea in its conflict with man. Rust, like a disease, would devour slowly and weaken where the direct onslaught of waves would not avail. Galvanizing, (the coating of iron with a skin of zinc), was man's only practical counter weapon to salt water rust. Could I substitute wood for any component of my pot? *Wood*, obviously, was cheaper than metal. It was immune to rust. But it was weaker. Could I substitute wood and still have the pot indestructible?

I had examined it in every detail. I had formed a mental picture of it with the bows made of hazels. I saw that if they were to collapse, hazels would not do. I substituted wood for the erecting and coupling bars. I saw that if they were to be as strong and efficient as iron they would have to be so thick that extra ballast would be needed to overcome their buoyancy. I might substitute wood for the slats of the bottom. But again they would have to be thick and clumsy, they would give buoyancy, and they could not possibly be as strong as my metal slats. I had been forced at last to the ironic conclusion that my pot as it stood was a perfect piece of mechanism, and that like a perfect work of art, there was nothing one could add to it, and nothing one could take away.

I was a stranger to Leeds. I was cold, hungry, dejected, still irresolute as to whether I should abandon the pot, or make another effort to obtain a reasonable quotation for making the experimental batch. Leeds made woollen goods I reflected as I made my way towards the main platform. There would be little chance of my finding a metal goods manufacturer here, and in any case it was far too late to make inquiries. But the thought of spending an hour in the station was unbearable, and I decided to put my suit-case and the pot in the cloakroom, go out and find a cafe and have a meal. I went to the cloakroom, and as I walked back down the platform towards the main entrance, I was startled by a feminine voice behind me. I turned to see a lady, and recognized her at once as a friend I had not seen for many years.

Little did I guess then in what peculiar way this lady was to lead me towards the solution of my problem. I was delighted to meet her. She was an actress. I learnt quickly that she was playing in a local repertory theatre, that she was broke, and was staying with an aunt out at

Headingley, that she was about to go to a cafe for a light meal before the show. Was I staying in Leeds? Would I care to go with her to a cafe and join her in a meal, and have a chat, and then come along to the show? I had no particular reason for continuing my journey to York that night. I could find a hotel in Leeds. I felt a great need to talk to someone, for sympathy. We walked out into the main street together.

There was no fog here. There was a suspicion of east wind that moved the air, and made it sting, like a too hot bath stings when you stir it with your limbs. There was no visible ice; but near the station was the astonishing spectacle of a policeman on point duty, standing with his back to a huge coke brazier. The street lamps, the lights of the trams, and of the few shops which remained open shone with the cold brilliance of arctic stars; and the very pavement exuded a cold that was more vicious than the cold of ice. We were too cold to speak while we walked.

We went into a multiple tea-shop, and sat down at a marble-topped table, with our shoulders against a steam radiator. The place had no fire but it was tropical compared with the temperature outside. I observed at once that my friend, who was very beautiful, looked pale and worried. She ordered a glass of malted milk and biscuits, and would not listen to my suggestions for something more seasonable and substantial. She was, quite unnecessarily it seemed to me, slimming. I had been thinking for a long while of steak and potatoes, but in sympathy I was obliged to ask for a poached egg and tea. We had a great deal to talk about, however, and if I detected a certain constraint on her part, a subtle impatience, as though she had some deep trouble of her own which she was bursting to tell me about, she gave me just that sympathy and encouragement I so badly needed.

She was deeply interested in what I told her about the inshore fisherman. She thought it was marvellous that I had invented something that would make their fishing safer and give new employment, and make a lot of money for myself, too. She agreed that an invention like mine ought to be worth millions. She thought that the Government instead of letting me go to the bother and expense of having the pots made should do it all for me, and pay me a good salary, too, for my expert advice. Mr. N, of course, was simply stupid. Yet I must take all that he said with a very big grain of salt. Most likely he had only talked like that to weaken my own idea of its value, which was the way of all business men. Theatrical managers in particular did that sort of thing so that you would take a smaller salary. I simply must not give up my invention. I must persevere and in the end everything was bound to come right. She felt about me exactly as she had felt about a certain young film actor of her acquaintance who couldn't even get a crowd part, and was absolutely down and out; and then suddenly a chance came, and he was now earning a hundred pounds a week in America.

I was heartened again. I wished that I had brought the pot with me so that I could have explained its advantages in greater detail; but I realized that I had been given a fair innings, and I set about finding the reason for my friend's unhappiness. It was an easy task. Like me she had been

181

longing to talk to someone about it, someone who would understand. She was in love with a man who had a part in the play I was to see, and while she believed that her love was really reciprocated, he had let himself become entangled with another member of the company, and they had just become officially engaged. It was tragic! The man was quite young, frightfully good-looking, and he was a magnificent actor, infinitely better than the one who was doing so well in America. He only wanted someone to push him along, to manage him, so that when his chance came, he would seize it. He wanted a woman behind him; but the right sort of woman, not the one he had got hold of, or rather the one who had got hold of him. She would simply hold him back. I would see and recognize that immediately I saw her. She was just a pretty doll, without an ounce of brain, or will-power or imagination, and she was perfectly hopeless as an actress.

I had no difficulty in identifying both the man and the other woman of this unhappy triangle. They appeared in the opening scene of the play. I thought that my friend might have been right about the woman, although she was extremely pretty and attractive. I felt that she was wrong about the man, who although he was very tall and handsome, did not appear to have much talent for acting. Yet the play was so bad it was difficult to form any fair opinion as to the merits of those who took part in it. It was the work I understood, of an anonymous amateur who had partly financed the production himself; and it was in the O'Neil manner, consisting of innumerable scenes and black-outs, but without unity, without drama, and, it appeared to me, without sense. Yet again my opinion of the play might have been unfairly influenced by the theatre, which seemed to be a converted nonconformist chapel, and was without any noticeable heating apparatus; and by the audience, which consisted of not more than thirty persons, all of whom, I presumed, had been given free seats, for they clapped with obvious insincerity at the end of every scene.

I soon found it almost impossible to concentrate on the actions and conversations of the shivering people who occupied the stage, and when my friend made an appearance she roused in me only a strong wish that I was in the train for York. The glow that she had given me had long since dissipated. I was assailed by the gloomiest thoughts, and I did not escape them when at the first genuine fall of the curtain I went round to the dressing-room and found my friend and was introduced to all the company except the man and his fiancée, who having no further part in the play had left the theatre. Rarely had I seen an unhappier company of human beings. If the theatre had been a chapel then this evidently had been the vestry. It was draughty and dingy, and the only source of heat was a tiny gas stove (with a bad leak) round which everyone was crowding.

I was unhappy myself, but I felt that these people were infinitely more so. They looked poor, ill, half-starved. I had a sudden impulse to do something kind for them. I asked my friend if she thought that anyone might like a drink. It was an unnecessary question. The only problem was to know what sort of drink and how to obtain it; and this was instantly solved by an elderly actor with a white face and a nasty cough who had appeared in one of the earlier scenes of the play. Everyone drank beer he said; there was a pub just round the corner, and the call-boy had just time to fetch some before the play continued. I thought it would be best to have a case. The boy returned two minutes before the interval ended; and in that time, in acknowledging a fervent toast proposed by the elderly actor, I consumed the contents of one large bottle.

I had never cared for beer; and I might have known that it was the worst possible drink for one whose reactions to alcohol were like mine. Before I had witnessed ten more minutes of that dismal play my depression had become an almost pathological melancholia. The theatre seats were hard, and there was no room to stretch one's legs. The air was so cold I might have been sitting waist deep in water. The only apparent effect of the beer on the actors and actresses was that they talked a little louder, but this produced an echo from the empty auditorium, and made what they said less coherent than before. My mind was completely detached from the play, however. I was aware of it only as a contributory physical annoyance. I reviewed with ever increasing despair, all the events of the day. I saw that my invention was a complete fiasco, that all the time and money I had spent on it had been thrown away, that instead of helping the fisherman to his feet again and making a fortune for myself, I had merely increased my financial difficulties and falsely raised the hopes of my fishermen friends. I felt that I'd never dare show my face in Bramblewick again.

And it appeared that I was not the only one on whom beer had a wholly morbid effect. I went round to the dressing-room when the curtain finally fell. I found the company, already muffled up in their coats, drinking what remained of the beer, and with that perversity which is one of the symptoms of the alcoholically affected mind, I yielded to my friend's persuasion to share the final bottle. She looked paler, sadder than when I had first met her. Suddenly she said that she was feeling very miserable, and would I mind very much if I saw her home? We could get a tram just at the bottom of the street and it was only about twenty minutes ride. I went out and got a taxi, and brought it round to the stage door; and I gave the driver the address in Headingley which my friend called out to me in a faltering voice as she got inside. As I got in myself I thought grimly of my last ride in a taxi; of how, full of confidence and hope I had set out that morning for my interview with Mr. N. But I was not permitted to think of my own misfortunes for long. Immediately the cab got under way my friend started to tell me all over again about her hopeless passion; and then, without warning, she burst into hysterical sobs. I felt profoundly sympathetic. There is nothing more tragic than unrequited love, and there is nothing less consolable by words. I didn't know what to say. I thought that if I admired the man it might make her loss seem greater; that if I suggested that he was unworthy of her she might dislike this even more. Finally I put my arms round her shoulders and let her cry against my chest.

Even for myself there was a certain comfort in that close contact with another human being. The taxi gave small protection from the cold. The windows leaked and the air that came through was like liquid ice, swirling about us. And my unfortunate friend seemed to find mental as well as physical comfort in my embrace, for after a while her sobbing quietened, and at last she drew her head away, dried her tears and powdered her nose. It seemed that we had reached Headingley. The cab drew up at the gates of an impressive house standing back from the road; but with lights visible in its lower front windows. The lights cheered me. I had a quick mental picture of the aunt, whom I imagined as a genial white-haired stoutish fussy person belonging to an age when slimming was unknown, thanking me for bringing her niece safe home on such a terrible night, asking me into a room where supper was laid in front of a roaring fire, and then firmly refusing to let me go back to Leeds and a cold hotel bedroom. We got out. I paid the driver, and he drove off. I opened the gates for my friend. She at once turned and put her hand in mine. She was terribly sorry that she could not ask me in, she said. Her aunt was an old maid, religious, and frightfully proper, and she would be shocked at the very thought of entertaining a man so late at night. She was so sorry that she had made a fool of herself, weeping like that. I had been so awfully kind and understanding, and she did so hope I would be successful with my invention. She was certain I would if I just stuck at it and refused to be discouraged by those dreadful business men. How was I going to get back? How silly she had been to let me dismiss the taxi. But if I hurried there was time to catch the last Leeds tram. I would find the tram-stop if I took the first turn to my left which would bring me into the main Otley-Leeds road. She would have just loved to have asked me in, but I understood, didn't I?

We said good-bye. I heard the screech of an electric tram, and I ran down the road, turned to my left down a narrow tree-planted lane, and reached the main road in time to see the car moving quickly away from the Stop: and while it bore no special legend, there was something in the very derisive sound it made that told me it was the last City bound tram of the night.

The road was what is known as a main arterial road. It was broad and straight and still maintained some of its surburban characteristics, for it was lighted, and there were private houses and gardens on each side. I did not know how far it was to Leeds. There was no means of finding out, for apart from the lights of the swiftly receding tram and one or two bedroom lights in the houses, there was no sign of stirring life. Looking in the direction of the tram, however, I detected a misty glow in the sky, and the tram itself was evidence that the city was there, although a long way off. I started to walk, thinking that if I followed the tramlines I could not go far wrong.

The frost was more intense than ever. The wind was rising and it cut through my clothes as though they were sacking. My feet were numb, so that even the smooth paving hurt like sharp pebbles. The fuddling effect of the beer soon passed off, but if my mind cleared it was only to give me a clearer aspect of my misfortunes, as the lifting of a fog reveals a lee shore to an anxious mariner. Again I reviewed the earlier events of the day, seeking for something on which to hang the slenderest hope. I sank into a peculiar alert trance, in which I was aware of all the physical discomforts of the cold, of the road I was walking on, the gleaming tram-lines, the lamps, the glow in the sky, yet in which I had also a perfect picture of my lobster pot. I examined it again in every detail, for something I could do without, or substitute with wood or some less costly material than iron. Apart from the galvanizing it was the base which had chiefly led me astray in my early estimate of costs. I appreciated now the immense labour I had put into it, the sawing of the lengths, the drilling of the holes, the riveting. Yet the base could not possibly be made of wood. If I substituted wood for the slats I should require just as many holes in the angle-iron frame to hold them, probably more. I must have iron for that frame, anyway. It seemed incredible that iron should be so expensive.

I looked at the tram-lines reaching as far ahead of me as I could see. There was enough steel in a yard of a single rail to make at least six of my pots: and there were miles of double rail, enough probably between where I was and the heart of Leeds to make a million pots. The lamp posts I passed were made of iron. Each of them had the material for a dozen pots. I passed by iron gates and iron palings, iron grids, iron man-hole covers, iron pillar boxes. I saw the skeleton of a new building that looked like a garage, and it was all of angle iron. Ships, locomotives, railways, motor cars, bridges, tools, machinery, domestic pots and pans, were all made chiefly of iron or steel. I was living in a new Iron Age. Yet it seemed that unless I could cheapen it in some way my invention must fail simply because of the prohibitive cost of this ubiquitous material.

I walked on and on through that night of record cold still in an alert trance, still seeing my lobster pot like a phantom in front of me; still concentrating fiercely on the problem of how it might be modified to make its manufacture practicable: yet all the time fully conscious of the physical world. The sky was now overcast. Little flakes of snow, like moths, were flying into the street lamps. I heard a distant clock strike twelve. Occasionally a motor car passed me, but travelling too fast for me to hold it up and ask for a lift. There were no trams in either direction, no visible human beings, and even in the houses, precious few lights. The road, however, with its gleaming tram-lines, led unfalteringly towards the glow in the sky; and although I had passed no shops, and the houses were still suburban, the glow was becoming appreciably nearer.

I did not see how I could cheapen the cost of manufacture without robbing the pot of most of its unique advantages. It must be instantly collapsible. It must be capable of quick erection. It must be rigid when erect. It must be capable of withstanding the destructiveness of the sea. I was being forced back again to the conclusion that it was not a practical thing, that I must give it up, and devote myself to the hateful task of writing again. I did not know how near I was to the solution of all my difficulties.

I was approaching a house which was either in course of construction, or was being extensively altered. It was divided from the road by an unmade garden, that was littered with timber, heaps of gravel and sand, and building material. The boundary wall of the garden at least was new. I saw as I reached it that it was made of a foundation of brick surmounted by a peculiar wooden structure which I did not at first consciously observe in detail, for my eyes were attracted by something lying just within a gateless entrance through the wall, where there was a heap of bricks, some drain pipes, a roll of heavy wire netting, and what appeared to be some iron gates. It was these which attracted me, not because they were gates, but because I recognized that they were, partly at least, made of angle iron of the same section as my original bed girders. There was a street lamp almost opposite the entrance. I stepped through. They *were* gates. They looked like the gates which (themselves netted) are used in the wire netting boundaries of tennis courts; and rolls of netting, and a pile of angle iron stakes close by confirmed this impression. What interested me, however, what made me oblivious to the fact that it was now snowing quite heavily, what shocked me instantly from my semi-trance, was the discovery that except for their size, they were identical in effect with the angle-iron frame of my base. Yet they were made, not in four pieces, riveted together, but from a single length of metal.

How?

I lifted one up, and looked at the corners. They were formed exactly like the corners of a picture frame, except that they were mitred only in one section of the L, the other section being bent at right angles: while at one corner the two free ends of the original length were gas welded. There were no holes, no rivets. Yet the whole thing was amazingly rigid and strong. With my size of frame it would be even stronger.

I gasped. If there was such a thing as a machine which would make the necessary mitre cuts at a single operation, then the amount of labour in making such a frame would be infinitesimal. It could be made at a fraction of the cost of mine, yet in effect it seemed stronger, so strong that I could dispense with metal slats and cross-piece for their strengthening value alone. All that I would have to do would be to fill in the space of the frame with something that was light, durable, that would keep lobsters out and keep them in. Manilla net would not do, because it would foul the bottom and tear: the same with wire netting unless of a very heavy gauge. It must be wood. But how should it be attached?

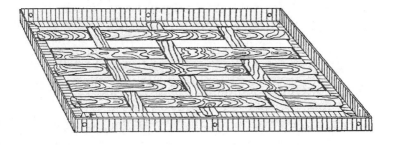

The 'bottom' of the final model showing plaited wooden strips held in place by their own tension

I turned towards the garden wall. It was as though the hand of destiny had suddenly pointed to that wooden super-structure, which previously I had observed only sub-consciously. I had never seen the like of it before. It consisted of long thin strips of wood, which were plaited in the manner of a fruit basket, over an upright strip, and under the next, making a structure of extraordinary strength. And more important than this even was the obvious fact that such strips could be plaited into my frame, without the use of any nails, meaning that I could dispense with the thirty holes and rivets required for the metal slats.

I examined the actual wood. It was common deal. Any sawmill could supply such material, and it would be absurdly cheap. I turned again to the gates to examine them for any mark that might afford a clue as to where they had been made. And suddenly I was startled by a stern authoritative voice behind me:

'Well, what's the game, young feller?'

I turned to see a burly policeman with his helmet and cape plastered in snow, standing in the garden entrance, looking at me intently: and I was immediately dazzled by the light of an electric torch which he flashed into my face.

A burglar with a bag of booty on his back might have found it easier to answer that question than I. To explain to the waiting policeman that I was the inventor of a collapsible lobster pot, and that I was examining the gates out of professional curiosity, because they and my pot were in an important respect similar, and this at midnight, and in a snow-storm, was to give him ample reason for locking me up as an escaped lunatic. Obviously however, some explanation was necessary, for I was trespassing; and there was every reason for him to suspect from my actions that I was at least loitering with felonious intent. He motioned me with his lamp to move out on to the pavement, into the full light of the street lamp. He stood very near to me, while I told him that having been spending the evening with a friend I had missed the last tram and was walking back to Leeds. I happened to be interested in the organization of a tennis club. I had noticed the doors and other material and I had stepped in to examine them; and I was just trying to find out where they had been made when he had spoken to me. I would willingly give him my name and address if he felt suspicious.

It was a weak invention. It struck me as soon as I had given it that it might lead to an awkward cross-examination. But the policeman, having taken a long look at me, had evidently formed his own conclusions, for he said, drily, with a thick Yorkshire accent:

'I should think tha's been having a jolly night of it with that friend of thine, eh? Plenty of beer?'

I was relieved. I had caught the familiar ironic idiom of the Yorkshireman; and it gave me his measure. I laughed.

'Enough,' I said, 'but it doesn't take long to wear off a night like this.'

To my greater relief he laughed too, although drily, and still with a certain suspicion in the way he was looking at me. But he seemed pleased with his own perspicacity.

'Aye,' he said, 'fire goes out, but you can still smell the smoke.'

He glanced suddenly towards the garden.

'What was it tha' was trying to find out about yon gates? Did tha' say that tha' was trying to find out where they were made?'

I replied that I was very anxious indeed to find a place where such things could be made cheaply. He gave me another searching look, but his last suspicions seem to have been allayed, for he replied, quite conversationally, that he knew where they were made, for he knew a man who worked for the firm and was actually on this very job. The firm was in Leeds. He believed that they made a special line of tennis court boundaries. He didn't know what their prices were, of course, but could give me the name and address. I crouched in the lee of the garden wall, while I wrote it down on a piece of paper which I put carefully away. I thanked the policeman. There was an awkward silence, during which I debated with myself as to whether it would be wise to offer him half a crown and say good night, or whether such an action might not be unfavourably construed. But the policeman himself relieved me of my embarrassment by remarking that it was a very cold night, and looked like getting worse, and that I'd best hurry along if I wanted to get to bed before morning. I thanked him again, and with a wild elation set off smartly in the direction of what I still believed was Leeds. But before I had taken half a dozen strides, he bawled after me:

'Hey! Did tha' say tha' was making for Leeds City?'

I stopped and turned. The policeman was grinning.

'Is that the way tha' was going before tha' stopped to look at yon gates?'

More than a suspicion of what had happened flashed

across my mind. I answered 'Yes.' He laughed.

'Eh! It will tak thee getting on eight years, to get round ta Leeds City that way, and tha'll need a ship when tha' comes to Atlantic Ocean. That's road to Otley. Tha's going opposite way to Leeds.'

He pointed his gloved hand in the direction from which I had come.

'That's the road to Headingley and Leeds,' he said, 'and it's a five-mile walk.'

It was a shock. I was already tired, and half-frozen and ravenous with hunger. The wind was increasing and with the snow was nearing blizzard strength. Yet the realization that I had at last solved the major manufacturing problem of my pot, that the thing was a thrilling possibility again, would have spurred me to any feat of endurance. I thanked the policeman again, and set off for Leeds.

BOOK THREE

1

I RETURNED to Bramblewick by the last train on the following night. My mission after all had been a complete success. I had called early in the morning on the firm whose name and address the policeman had given me. I had demonstrated my lobster pot to a work's manager who from the first had shown enthusiasm, intelligence, and a keen desire to do business. I had explained the modifications of the base due to my nocturnal discoveries. He had said without hesitation that his firm could undertake the manufacture of the first batch and at the lowest possible price. He had suggested further that we should have a base frame made at once so that I could watch it through its various stages, and thus be assured that the pattern of the rest of the batch would be correct.

He was a young man, evidently proud of the responsible position he held, proud of his firm and its equipment, of its workmen. He led me into a workshop that was spacious, well ventilated yet warm: and despite that the roof windows were caked with the snow which was still falling heavily, well lighted by the light of day.

There was an electric forge, a long engineers' bench where several men were working: another bench where three begoggled men were engaged with oxy-acetylene welding plant. There were lathes, drills, grinders, and many other machines whose purpose I could not guess. On the cement floor, however, and in a pile at one end of the shop, were door frames such as those I had seen in the garden in various stages of completion. There was noise, but not the hellish clamour of the Birmingham stamping shop. The machines seemed docile. The sturdy, healthy looking men seemed the masters of them. They

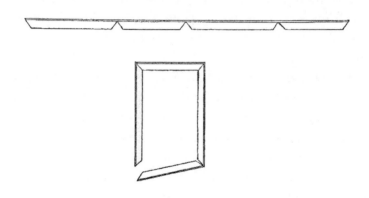

Above: Bar of angle iron with mitre notches cut
Below: Frame partly made, open end to be closed
and welded

talked and whistled as they moved about. Their movements were the movements of free men.

The manager spoke to one of the acetylene welders, who was also youthful and had a pleasant smile. I put the pot on the bench while the manager explained what I required. The man at once measured the base, then picked up a bar of angle iron, marked it, and moved to a machine, which, but for its size, was like the device that is used in offices for stamping stationery with an embossed legend. He placed one end of the bar between its jaws, pulled down a lever and let it go again. The end of the bar was sliced diagonally, as simply and as neatly as though it had been cardboard. He moved the length along to the next mark, and worked the lever again. This time the cut did not go across the whole section of the bar. It merely bit out a triangular notch from one section, and this operation was repeated at three other points. Finally the other end of the bar was given a complete diagonal cut.

He lifted the bar and fastened one end in a vice. He bent the length forward with his hands and, where the first notch came, formed a perfect corner like that of a picture frame. He repeated this with the other two. The iron bar became a frame, with the diagonal cuts meeting in the fourth corner. He clamped the frame in the vice again, so that the free ends were forced tightly together. Then he pulled the goggles over his eyes, lighted the burner of the welding apparatus, and with a thin metal rod held close to the joint, brought the jet of the burner close, so that the rod fused into the molten edges of the angle iron, and the frame was completely joined.

I had dispensed with the corner rivet holes, and those for the metal slats, but the holes for the hinging of the bows were still necessary. These he punched out with a hand machine, scarcely bigger than a pair of garden shears, and as easily as a tram conductor punches a ticket. The frame was complete. Its making had occupied less than five minutes.

The manager had apologetically explained then that the mechanic who would make the remaining parts of the pot was at present engaged on an important 'promised' job and would not be free until after dinner: but if I called about three the whole thing would be finished, and if I liked I could have it galvanized. He did not know how much galvanizing would cost as it was done outside the firm. It would not be very expensive, however. He could supply the batch of twenty pot frames within ten days, and the inclusive cost would be *five shillings apiece.*

It was snowing heavily at Bramblewick, and still freezing hard; but the wind, while strong, was blowing west of north, and as soon as I got out of the station, I knew that the sea was comparatively smooth, for it made no sound. I carried my suit-case, and my old pot and the frame of the new one inside the sail-cloth case. I walked quickly past the rows of smug Up-Bank villas to the Bank top, and saw the old town packed beneath me, with the cheerful cottage lights gleaming here and there, and the cottages themselves and the mad pattern of alley ways, made visible by the light of the street lamps, shining on the fallen snow.

Some lads, with home-made sledges, were toiling up the Bank, shouting and quarrelling. As I came near them they stopped to stare at me in the traditional Bramblewick way, and I knew, by their sudden silence, what to expect as soon as I had passed them, and turned my back: for I saw one lad, the son of an Up-Bank skipper, already making a snowball. They were better clad, and a little smoother of talk than the lads who had been my contemporaries, yet it seemed that the old spirit remained, for they threw their snowballs with derisive shouts and taunts, and I recognized an insulting phrase which I had shouted after strangers in the brief period of tolerance I had enjoyed before I had 'won' my scholarship. In those days, however, the throwing would have been better, for the accepted technique of snowball-making was to begin with a core of a stone, which enabled one to press the snow to an ice-like consistency, giving it weight, and making it far more effective both in flight and in striking power.

I hurried down out of range. I was glad to be back in Bramblewick. I reached the Road, which was nearly a foot deep in snow, and turned up an alley on my right, which brought me after many twists and turns to the beginning of my own alley. Here I encountered Jane Allinson, with a shawl over her head and carrying a bucket of coal, which she had evidently brought from the gas-house. She gave me a quick look of curiosity: and I thought for once I would anticipate her inevitable greeting, and said:

'Now then, have you been getting some coal from the gas-house?'

But she replied, unperturbed:

'Aye. Are you just coming from the railway station? It's cold weather, isn't it?'

I was glad to be back. As I unlocked my cottage door,

the door of the Brewsters' was opened, and Reub put his head out, and I imagined that he was staring hard at the case containing the pots.

'Now then,' he said, 'you've got back all right.'

'Aye,' I answered, 'it's a cold night.'

'Aye,' he agreed as he popped inside again.

I opened my door, and my nostrils were assailed by the smell of damp walls and furniture, mixed with the smell of soot, and there was such a chill in the room that I gasped. I lit the gas, however, and looking about me, at the cold disordered fireplace, at the table still littered with the utensils of my last meal, at the settee on which my sea-boots and oilskins once more reposed, I felt glad even to be back here, although I was not going to stay. I was in a fever to get round to Marney, to surprise him by my sudden reappearance, to hear all his news, to give him mine, to show him the new pot, to hear his excited comments. It was nearly supper-time too, and I had bought in Leeds a contribution to that meal in the shape of a large pork pie. I unpacked this, changed into my oilskins and sea-boots, turned out the gas, and hurried out again.

The shops were closed. The village was entirely deserted to the storm. In the Dock the snow lay so thick it had almost submerged the launching wheels of the cobles, and there was a drift against the doors of the lifeboat house, at least six feet in depth. Yet the sea made little sound. So long as the wind kept west of north and off the land this was possible fishing weather, and for a certainty the Lunns would have been to sea to-day for the first haul of their pots. Had they done well, I wondered?

I hurried up Chapel Street. There was a light in Marney's window. I had a sudden fear that Tom Fosdyck might be there, and staying for supper. My fear proved groundless however. Marney and Amy were alone. Yet my appearance lacked the drama of complete surprise, for the first thing Marney said was:

'Hello, here you are. I was just coming round to fetch you. Tom Fosdyck came in a few minutes ago and told us he'd heard you'd got here by the last train. Get your things off and sit down by the fire. Amy was just going to start getting supper.'

It was good to be back again, to feel that I was with real friends, in a real home. It was good to see Marney's weather-beaten face, and his clear eyes: to look at Amy and see that peculiar beauty which is found nowhere but in the face of a woman who has got the man she loves, and borne him a child. She was knitting a garment for the bairn. Marney had been at work on the competition rug when I entered, but he promptly put this down as I moved to the fire, and I was aware that he was looking at the lobster pot case out of the tail of his eye. I felt, however, that my own news would not spoil for a little keeping; and I knew that Marney was far too polite to question me until I gave him a direct cue. I put the bag under the table, and I did nothing but offer him a fag. I observed as he took it that he lacked some of his customary cheerfulness, and Amy promptly confirmed this impression, for she remarked:

'Well, I'm glad you're back again safely, and I hope you've had a nice time where you've been, and the weather hasn't been so bad as it's been here. Only I do hope you've something cheerful to talk about. *He* hasn't. He's been in such a temper all day, I've felt like clearing out and leaving him. *He* seems to think he's the only one that suffers when things go wrong. And half of it's just childishness. It doesn't worry him that he hasn't brought a brass farthing into the house all week. He's only in a bad temper because he thinks that the Fosdycks are up on the Lunns to-day.'

Marney, more obviously than ever, was a man with a grievance. It did not require much art on my part to get him to explain what it was. I asked him if they had got all their pots safely shot yesterday morning.

'You'd well ask him that!' Amy said tartly. 'That's what started it all.'

'Aye,' Marney said. 'We got them shot all right. We put them in deep water, on mud, so that they'd be safe if it came on to blow, and where they'd stand a chance of a very good catch of crabs. It was freezing hard, but the sea was like a mill pond. We couldn't have had a better day for it. But we hadn't time to shoot any lines of course, and anyway cod have been so scarce lately that father reckoned it would only be a waste of time and bait. The Fosdycks aren't ready to start potting for another month. They'd gone with lines of course, and damned if they didn't get the biggest catch they've had for years. They nearly filled the coble bottom. And to crown all, cod were bringing two bob a stone more than they've fetched this winter. And there we were with nowt. And the Fosdycks laughing at us.'

'They had more reason to laugh at you this morning though,' said Amy.

'Aye,' Marney agreed. 'We thought we'd take our lines too, and come back with a load of fish, as well as a load of crabs; and we were baiting our lines till after dark last night. We launched down at about six o' clock this morning, with the tide half ebb. Weather was clear then, and it had stopped snowing. The Fosdycks went off first, leaving us with the coble just awash. We got in and pushed off, and then damn it, the engine wouldn't start. Father split his finger with the starting handle, and nearly heaved it at John's head he was that crazed. We tried everything to make it go. And it took us nearly two hours to find out the pump had frozen, and that it wouldn't go at all. And there we were! We couldn't haul the coble back by ourselves. We daren't leave her and go off in the small boat. We just had to mess about all morning until the Fosdycks came back, and damned if they didn't have another big catch. Aye, they had so much fish that we had to help them to gut it and carry it up to the Dock. But it won't happen again, *I* know. I went down just before dark, and tied an old sea-coat round that damned pump. I tell you we'll get twice as much fish as the Fosdycks to-morrow, as well as half a dozen kits of crabs. If only the wind doesn't get round north-east. Anyway, what about supper, Amy. What are we going to have? I'm damned if I'm going round to the fish shop for it, not when it's what the Fosdycks have caught.'

I produced the pie, and it was the cue that Marney had been waiting for.

'God, that's a bit of all right, and no mistake,' he said. 'It'll be champion with some fried taties and Yorkshire Relish, won't it, Amy? . . . But that's not the only thing you've got to show us,' he went on eagerly. 'What about that shut-up pot. How did you get on with that chap at Birmingham? Did you get a fleet of them made. How much are they going to cost? Is that the old one you've got in the bag?'

Amy got up. I began to unpack the case. Marney moved quickly to the street door, locked it, and then stood eagerly watching me while I pulled the new pot out. It was not netted of course. There was nothing of it yet that was Marney's. I braced myself for an immediate adverse criticism. I saw that he was staring with a terrible concentration, at the modified base with its plaited wood strips, instead of the iron slats of the original model. I anticipated his expected criticism. I explained that the iron slats had proved too expensive in material and labour, and I had found that with the angle iron frame properly made we could, dispense with them, and that the wood strips were there not to give strength to the whole pot but merely to stop lobsters getting in and out the wrong route. But to my surprise and relief he remarked quickly:

'I reckon it's a hundred per cent better having them like that. Why didn't you think of it before? It's a champion idea. You know I've said from the very first that the closer you kept to our pot, the better this one will fish. I reckon it's a hundred per cent better having the bottom made of wood. Lobsters are very easily frightened remember. A bottom made of iron is bound to make a noise if the whole pot's shaking in a strong tide, and it's quite likely to frighten them away.'

He took hold of the whole frame, tested its weight,

pressed his fist against the plaited wood, laid the contraption on the table and opened and closed it. Then he remarked with more eagerness than I had ever dared to hope for:

'It's champion. I tell you it's a thousand per cent better like that. I like the galvanizing, too. It gives the whole thing a finish. Damn it, I'd be half afraid of putting a thing like that in the sea. It's as pretty as an ornament. Look at it, Amy,' he added, turning to his wife, who was just putting the frying-pan on the fire, 'Come and look at it.'

'I've no time to look at it now. How many eyes do you think I've got. Can't it wait till after supper?'

Marney shrugged his shoulders, and turned to the pot again.

'God,' he said, 'I'm just dying to see how it looks when it's netted. I've got plenty of twine over here, and a needle. I'll set to as soon as we've finished supper, and I'll have it done before bedtime. And I'll make a better job of it than I did of the first pot. I only hope Tom Fosdyck doesn't pop in again. He knows there's summat in the breeze, or he wouldn't have come in like that—just to let us know you'd got back. Who made it for you, that chap you went to see? You can tell us all about it while we're having supper. God, I bet he was surprised to see you fetch a lobster pot out of that bag.'

We had to put the pot away to make way for the supper things. During that meal, which had none of the physical and mental constraints of my last night's meal in Leeds, I recounted such of my adventures as I thought would be of interest to the company.

Amy expressed her admiration for my courage in going to see such a famous person as Mr. N. She herself would have been so terrified at being taken into his presence, she'd have been quite dumb, and very likely would have fainted; and fancy having to find your way about in big towns like Birmingham and Leeds, and not knowing a soul!

'Aye,' Marney agreed. 'But it's education that does it you know. It's what I've always said. A good education will take a chap anywhere, and make him afraid of no one. But it beats me about that chap, thinking such a lot about the pot at first, and then not wanting to have anything more to do with it. God, I bet he'll rue it. I bet the day will come when the sight of a lobster will turn him sick, because it will remind him that he let a fortune slip past his nose. There *is* a fortune in that pot. If you can get a few of them made as cheap as that, think how cheap they'll come for big numbers! You're going to sell millions. . . I'm just dying to see what it looks like when it's netted. Do you know what's happened to that needle, Amy?'

Amy indignantly refused my offer to help her with the washing-up. She found Marney his ball of twine and the needle, and I joined him at the fireside. He filled the needle, took the pot between his knees, and began. And once more I yielded to the fascination of his hands. Amy joined us shortly. None of us spoke for a long time. I felt extraordinarily happy. All my troubles seemed to be over. The manager had promised that I should have the whole batch within a fortnight at the outside. It would take perhaps three days to net them. We would start fishing with them at once, and the Government Inspector would be able to carry out his final test. It would be impossible for him to report otherwise than favourably. The money Mr. N had stated as being the minimum for taking out world patents and organizing a private company would be a paltry sum for Mr. X. Once that company was established there would be no need to co-operate with any other firm. We would manufacture the pot ourselves in our own factory, and that factory would be situated not in the heart of a grimy city like Birmingham, but on the coast, in ideal surroundings. It would be a model factory too; planned for maximum mechanical efficiency, yet affording maximum comfort for its workers, who would be regarded as human beings, not as spiritless slaves. Wages would be high. Encouragement would be given to the workers to save, and invest their savings in the firm, so as to share in its profits. There would be reading-rooms, and a gymnasium and a sports' ground, and a social club. As for the fishermen themselves, they would ask nothing more than to be able to pursue their own profession at the economic return my invention would assure them. You might search every grade of human society, and not find a happier home than this of Marney Lunn's. . . They were poor. The winter's cod season had resulted in a dead loss. But (perhaps because they were poor) they were generous and proud, and whenever I brought in a packet of tea or a loaf, so that my own meals would not be an extra burden on their larder, I had always to make some discreet excuse. They made no outward show of affection for each other. Amy could nag; Marney could be moody and irritating. They were both capable of a domestic row, which might, in private come to blows. What was this, however, but the shading, the necessary relief to a deep passionate love which had its origin in a sound physical affinity, which had been seasoned by the anxieties, the hardships, the joys they had shared, and above all by the birth of their child. I would not, I thought, like Marney to earn too much money. Neither he nor Amy would be so happy in that Up-Bank villa of Marney's cross-word puzzle dream. Yet the gulf that separated them from that, was wider than what lay between them now and stark poverty. If my pot only served to widen this gulf, to relieve Amy of the strain of knowing whether next week's rent or food bill could be paid it would have achieved something fine.

The netting grew like magic from Marney's hands. He covered the ends and 'roof', made the spouts, and stretched them into the pot. He made the doors, tied the bait-string in, and at last took a sock from the clothes-line below the mantelpiece and put it in as a dummy bait. Then as before, he put it on the table, and looked at it as an artist looks at a finished canvas. For myself there was not quite the same thrill there had been in the completion of the first full sized model. I had taken no part whatever in its actual making; and there was no suspense as to whether it would work or not, for mechanically it was identical with the other. Yet it was equally beautiful and Marney's own enthusiasm was a climax in itself. He took a fag from me, lit it, and expelled the first mouthful of smoke at the pot. He leaned forward and collapsed it; then erected it and sat back.

'God—it looks good,' he said fervently. 'I knew it would, but I didn't think I'd like it quite so much. That wood has improved it. I was never quite satisfied with those iron slats. It looks more like one of our pots, and it would look even better if you had two sticks down the sides, although I know it wouldn't shut up if you had them. Those are even better spouts than the last ones I made. They stretch differently when you have them and the net all in one piece; and it takes you a bit of practice to get the knack of it; I bet the next one will be even better still. I tell you if we had only sixty of them ready now, we'd catch enough lobsters the first week's fishing to make up for all we've lost on cod. That pot will fish better than any of ours. It wouldn't surprise me if it caught four lobsters to our one. I'm dying to see how it will fish. You know we've never yet given the full sized one a trial.'

He paused, but added quickly:

'Now look here, why shouldn't we take this one with us to-morrow morning, and put it among ours, and see how many crabs it will catch. You could come with us if you liked. We could do with a spare hand hauling those pots in deep water. We'll be away at daybreak unless the wind gets round nor'-east.'

He looked at me with a questioning smile.

The snow and the frost, and the bleak morning sea, seemed very remote before this blazing fire. There was a sound of wind, but it was still off shore: the surf was scarcely audible. I assented eagerly. Amy at once put her knitting down, and remarked with a yawn:

'Well, if you're going off at daybreak, you'll want to get to bed early. It's time I fed the bairn too.'

I got up. Marney got up too, and we packed the pot.

'I'll walk down to the Dock with you,' he said. 'I always like to see what the weather's doing before I turn in. I won't be a minute, Amy.'

He took hold of the pot to collapse it and as he did so gave it a last admiring look:

'God,' he muttered. 'That's a champion pair of spouts. Champion. I bet that pot will fill itself with crabs, first shot. I reckon a pot like that will catch owt!'

2

It seemed quite dark when Marney awakened me by shouting up my bedroom stairs:

'Ahoy! Come down as quick as you can. The cobles are snowed up, and we've got to dig them out. Don't forget your pot.'

Five minutes later I had joined the Lunns and the Fosdycks in the Dock.

There was still only the faintest sign of day. The overhead sky was cloudless however, and starry, and the fallen snow gave all the illumination necessary for the task of clearing a way from where the cobles were lying to the line of last night's high-water mark on the Slipway, where the snow was comparatively thin. The wind was north and strong, yet still apparently off-shore. A sound came from the sea, but it was low and even, indicating nothing worse at present than a ground-swell breaking on the scaur-ends: although I knew from experience that this was the sound which so often preceded the north-easter.

Shovels and picks had been borrowed from the lifeboat house. Without a word, Marney thrust a shovel into my hand and I fell to, heaving the snow which he and Luke Fosdyck loosened with picks from the Fosdyck's coble, which was the first to be launched. The snow was frozen and brittle as glass. It was hard to get a purchase on it. The wood handle of the shovel was so cold to my ungloved hands it seemed to burn. Yet there was a peculiar excitement in it all that made me oblivious to physical discomfort. I had once more the sense of an attack, that an enemy lay in the dark beyond the Slipway, compelling a stealthiness, a quiet, as though his outposts were alert within hearing distance. And this time I was among the attacking party, not a spectator. I had thrown my pot in the bows of the motor coble before Marney had accosted me.

We cleared the Fosdycks' coble, and dragged and pushed her to the Slipway top. Then we steadied her down the icy slope to the beach, and dragged and pushed her again to the water's edge, and launched her from the wheels. Even the beach was thinly covered with snow. There was ice on the shallow salt water pools, the weed was frozen and brittle, and crunched under one's boots like frozen fern. We had to drag the wheels back to the Dock, for the tide was flowing. We cleared the motor coble and launched her down. The Fosdycks' coble was now awash. We helped them to put into her about a score of heavy stones for ballast; then helped to push the boat off, until she floated. They rowed away quickly into the darkness. The whole of this time I had heard no one speak.

But as we seized hold of the motor coble, to push her out from shallow water, I heard John remark, grumbling and antagonistic:

'I bet they're going to shoot along to High Batts. That's where they got all that fish yesterday: and I reckon that's why they're in such a hurry to be off, in case we may happen to have our lines in the coble, and might beat them to it. Why the hell do we always let them get off first?'

To which Marney muttered sarcastically:

'Women and children first!'

And Henry said, with his habitual politeness:

'They're old men, Luke and Tindal. I don't envy them a good catch or two, seeing how bad they've done this winter. I only hope they have another.'

To which Marney rejoined:

'Garn. You know damned well Luke and Tindal are both of them hoping our engine won't start, and that we'll have another do like yesterday.'

Apart from Marney giving me the shovel, none of the Lunns had made the slightest sign that he was aware of my presence. As soon as the coble was well afloat, we got in, and without waiting to be told, I moved for'ard out of everyone's way, and with my hands I shovelled the snow from a triangular space in the high bows, and settled down, using my folded lobster pot for a seat. The sky had paled rapidly during the launching, and I could see my companions clearly. Henry had the boat-hook in his hands, and was keeping the coble head seawards. John was priming the engine, and suddenly he bent down to the starting handle. It was a tense moment. The engine coughed, and was silent. But at the second attempt it started. He opened the throttle, let it run for a minute, then put in the clutch, and we headed down the Landing fairway for the marking posts and the open sea.

I had been out with the Lunns, many times before, and in most sorts of weather, but I soon realized that this was to be a new experience. My body at least had been warmed by the exertion of launching and carrying the gear, but before we had passed the Posts, all this warmth oozed from me, and a numbness attacked my feet and hands, and spread up my limbs so that I felt I was being frozen to the structure of the boat, and that soon movement of any kind would be impossible. My excitement remained, however: and the sense that we were engaged on a raid on an enemy's domain grew stronger as we reached the ends of the sheltering scaurs and the coble rose and sank on the living sea. My companions too, were tense now, and increasingly alert. Henry steered, John was at the engine, Marney was preparing some pot bait, but each of them glanced repeatedly at the paling sky, and to the seaward horizon. For this was the time, close upon dawn, that the weather invariably revealed its plans. Already the whole coast of the Bay was visible, its cliffs, on which the snow secured but a sparse hold, appearing almost black against the white of the fields and moors. The shore was white, and there was snow in patches almost to the water's edge where the scaur ends became black again among the surf. The wind mysteriously had dropped. The overhead sky in which a few stars remained visible was still cloudless, but looking to the north-east, along the shoulder of Low Batts, I saw that the dividing line between sea and sky was obscured by a vast wall of cloud, so dark and solid in its foundations, so high where its serrated contours cut the sky, that it might have been the coast-line of another country, whose sea-cliffs rose up to a hinter-land of wild and inaccessible hills; and completing that illusion, the skyward lines of the cloud mass were now edged a pure white by the reflected light of the still invisible sun, giving an aspect of snowclad peaks of immense altitude.

I was familiar with that type of cloud formation. It signified above everything a change. In summer it would presage a period of fierce thunderstorms and torrential rain terminating a heat wave or a spell of cold. But in winter while thunder was not infrequent, the usual development was a freshening sea wind, with squalls of hail or snow, that might drop to a hard frost and a clear sky when the sun went down, or grow to a gale and a blizzard.

Henry was staring hard towards the north-east. 'It's going to snow again before long,' he said quietly.

'Aye. More than snow,' said John. 'That's a mucky carry-on over there. If there isn't a wind in all that, it will be a wonder to me. I wish to God we'd got our lines and not bothered with the pots. There'll be a hell of a swell running out there, before we've got them hauled. We'll be lucky if we can get one fleet. The Fosdycks will have the laugh on us again.'

'Garn,' put in Marney. 'If we'd brought our lines we'd have caught nowt. The Fosdycks won't do that three times running, I know. I reckon they'll be lucky if they get a basketful to-day, and I reckon we'll be doing poorly if we don't get six barrels of crabs.'

We were now about half a mile from the Landing, steaming almost straight out to sea. There was still no wind, but the swell was definitely growing, for occasionally I felt the sting of spray whipping over the bows, and the coble pitched violently. Suddenly Marney seemed to remember my existence, for he shouted,

'Eh! Did you fetch your patent pot with you?'

Both Henry and John too acknowledged my existence by grinning, and Henry shouted:

'How did you get on with that chap at Birmingham? I heard Marney say summat about a pot when we were in the Dock, but we had too much trouble digging that snow away for me to ask him about it. Have you got it there? Come along aft so that we haven't to shout above the engine.'

I was cramped where I was, the snow had melted round my thighs and wet me to the skin; I was benumbed, my teeth were chattering and I had a powerful reluctance to move, even when a sea struck the bow and sent a shower of spray down my neck. I got up, however, and took the pot aft.

I felt that even to have given the barest outline of my adventures at Birmingham and Leeds would have been impossible under the circumstances. I told Henry that I had succeeded in finding a manufacturer who would make the batch for the test, and that this one was a sample. . . . I had kept it in the case. Marney obliged by opening it and putting the pot on top of the engine box; and he obliged me further by erecting it. It might have been simply that I was so cold, but I was entirely without confidence in my invention at that moment. It looked so startlingly new, and in spite of Marney's handiwork, obviously manufactured and the product of landsmen. It looked absurdly incongruous here in the wildly pitching coble, in the presence of these practised men of the sea, moving out towards that challenging, ominous horizon: and I imagined that there was a faint contempt in Henry Lunn's eyes, as he glanced at it, then looked at the sea ahead, and at the pot again. But his first comment was reassuring.

'Aye. They've made it just as good as that one you made yourself, only you've got a wood bottom in it haven't you? They've made it more like ours. I think that's better than having it all of iron, and it looks just as strong. It looks champion. And I bet it will fish, too. I bet it will fish better than ours.'

'It's a big improvement having a wood bottom,' was John's comment.

'That's what *I* told him when I saw it first,' said Marney. 'The closer he can get to *our* pots the better. I thought we'd put it in the middle of one of our fleets and give it a try-out. I reckon it will fill itself with crabs. And I reckon it will do better still with lobsters.'

'It stands to reason it will,' Henry agreed. 'I only wish we had three fleets of shut-up pots ready for when we go close in for lobsters first spell of fine weather.'

'So do I,' said John. 'They'll be easier to haul. They're lighter than ours.'

'They'll be easier to clean too,' said Marney. 'You're going to get crabs and lobsters out in half the time with there being no ballast in the way.'

'Did you have any time to spare in Birmingham or Leeds?' inquired John. 'Did you see any musical instrument shops?'

I was able to inform him that I had made inquiries at no less than three such shops, and that sundry price lists and information on the matter of brass band instruments awaited him at my cottage on our return.

Marney put a cod's head in the bait string of my pot, tied the door, and laid it on the coble bottom out of the way.

'It's time we were seeing our buoys,' he remarked, looking ahead. 'It will be dead slack tide. They ought to be showing.'

We were still going due east. Day had broken, but there had been no visible sunrise. Gradually the mass of cloud upon the horizon had lost its mountainesque contours, and had deteriorated into a lower and more even type of cloud, which, spreading west had overcast the entire sky in a uniform grey. There was a faint suspicion of north-east wind. The swell was increasing, and, as Marney hailed the discovery of the first buoy, came the first sparse snowflakes.

I was heartened by Henry's comment upon the pot; and as we approached the buoy, and Marney stood ready to gaff it, I forgot, temporarily, that I was cold. For me the excitement of deep water fishing is in the sense it gives of communication with that territory which is perpetually hidden under the opaque substance of the sea: a territory which is, in effect, more remote from human comprehension than the stars. Soundings may give us its general configurations; trawls may reveal the nature and trend of its areas of rock, and sand and ooze, and give us much knowledge of its inhabitants. Man himself, with various contraptions, has penetrated into this territory: to salve ships, to regain what the sea, with its treachery and might has taken from man, to take the sea's own riches. Yet the astronomer with his telescope has a more certain picture of some infinitely remote planet than the diver obtains when he moves within closely prescribed range along the bottom of the sea, where the light is obscure, and there is no real perspective, and where, except in the clearest and calmest water, his one reliable perceptive sense is the blind man's sense of touch.

Marney pulled the buoy into the coble. John at once stopped the engine. Henry seized the rope from Marney's hands, put it over the pulley of a short, primitive derrick lashed over the gunwale near the stern, Marney and John took hold of it, and all three started hauling. It was hard gruelling work. I would have helped, but it seemed that there was no room for me to get a purchase on the rope, and no one directed me. The coble had swung round stern on to the swell and the growing wind. They were not merely hauling at a lobster pot. The main rope, or tow, to which the pots at regular intervals were attached, was anchored at each end, and they were actually hauling the coble itself against this anchorage, and against the swell and the wind: and I saw what power the boat exerted whenever its stern reared up, for they had to let the tow slip back, lest with its rough, tarry, sand ingrained surface it should saw the flesh from their hands, that seemed inadequately protected with woollen mitts. It was now snowing heavily. This made their task more difficult, for even with my hands free, I found it hard to keep a foothold on the slippery bottom boards. I wedged myself in between a thwart and the gunwale, watching the slowly ascending tow, and my admiration for these three men, and for the breed of men they typified grew even deeper. They were fighters, with the sea their eternal enemy. They were strong, audacious, brave, above all indomitable. Their contest with the sea was an even contest. The sea took, but they forced the sea to give; and it was not the sea directly that was beating them now, but the economic conditions that governed the price of their catch, of their bait and gear. There was a glamour in this strenuous hauling of pots on a winter's morning; there was a pride in fighting the sea in an open boat, with a storm growing, and a perilous bar dividing sea from haven. There was the stuff to give a swagger to a man's walk ashore, and put that look of the conqueror in his eye that would make him irresistible to women. But to the fish buyer, to the fishmonger, to the housewife in a city remote from the sound of the sea, there was no appreciable difference in fish caught in wild weather from an open boat, at the risk of men's lives, and fish caught in a calm by a well-equipped trawler. All that concerned them was the quality of the fish, its cheapness and a plentiful supply.

There must be no more of this hauling pots by hand I thought. There must be no more fishing from an open coble in such conditions as these. My pot would make hauling a simpler and a lighter task, but even so a motor winch would be quicker and more efficient. And the breed of the men would not suffer if they were made more comfortable by having a cabin to go into for a spell of warmth and rest, where on a morning like this there would be a stove burning, and hot coffee and tea.

The sea here was deep. They must have been hauling for at least fifteen minutes before the first anchor was lifted aboard and the 'strop' of the first pot came within reach. Marney stopped hauling on the main tow, and seized the 'strop'. Then he leaned over the gunwale, lifted the pot in, and laid it dripping on a thwart. It contained about a dozen fair-sized crabs.

He had already dispensed with his hauling mitts. He opened the door of the pot, put in his bare hand, quickly seized the nearest crab, jerked it through the door, and into a 'crib' next to the thwart. He then put in his hand for another, dextrously avoiding the wicked-looking claws. He was grinning.

'Not bad for a new pot,' he said, as he went on removing the catch. 'We don't expect a new pot to fish properly until it's been in the sea for at least a week. If they'd been old ones they'd have been bursting with crabs. I tell you you'll have to go a long way to beat these pots of ours for fishing.'

I was thinking the same thing, and I glanced uneasily at my own pot. I had hoped that it would fish better than the old type. I suddenly felt that I should be content if it fished as well. Marney took out the last crab, put a lump of fish in the bait string and tied up the door. Henry and

John meanwhile had continued hauling at the tow, and now Henry shouted:

'Hurry up there. Here's another pot.'

Marney pushed the first one across the thwart towards me.

'It will save us a lot of time if you can help,' he said. 'Stow this one as far forrard as you can, right up where you were sitting. Make a neat job of it. There's twenty-nine more of 'em to come.'

The coble was pitching more wildly than ever. The showers of spray which broke continuously over the stern, made a thick slush of the fallen snow, more slippery than ice. It required two hands to lift the pot, and I had to climb over two thwarts, with the 'strop' dangling behind: and, after my own slender pot, it seemed that this one weighed at least a quarter of a hundredweight. Yet as I struggled with it, I found satisfaction in the thought that this was one of the many ways in which my invention would score. There would be no need to stack them. They would lie in a neat pile in the stern part of the boat, all ready for shooting again. The advantage under conditions such as these would be immense.

I stowed the pot, but Marney wasn't satisfied, and he made me lift it up and stow it a different way round. He had removed the catch of the second pot by the time I had climbed back aft, and it was ready for me when the third pot came up. I had just time to see that this one, like the second, contained about a dozen crabs.

The hauling went on. The wind had freshened to a breeze. The sea was steadily growing, but I knew the Lunns too well to imagine that they would turn homewards until their job was done, unless the wind reached gale force. The pots continued to average about a dozen crabs each. Not one had less than nine, and one had sixteen. I continued to help with the stowing. By the time the last pot of that fleet was hauled, the coble was piled up, like a hay cart, and as John started the engine and we turned into the weather, we shipped a sea that washed three of the topmost ones clean overboard and, despite our oilskins, wet us through. We had to bring to while the pots were hauled back, and their 'strops' and the tow cleared. Then as we had already drifted on to unfished ground, Henry gave the order to start shooting.

It was a quicker job this, for it was done under full steam, but it was infinitely more perilous. The tow was coiled at one side of the boat. From this the short 'strops' ran to their respective pots in what appeared to me to be the utmost confusion. John had to pay away the tow. As he came to a 'strop,' Marney had to seize the pot to which it belonged, lift it clear of the rest and heave it over at the exact moment its 'strop' tightened with the speed of the boat.

I had moved up into the stern, close to Henry to be out of the way. Still with the helm under his left arm he was keeping close watch on his two sons, while cunningly dodging the heaviest of the seas, to keep the boat as steady and as dry as possible.

'This is when your sort of pot is going to be most useful to chaps like us,' he remarked, 'when we're shooting at full speed in a growing sea. It's not often an accident happens, I know. If you always stow your pots the same way, you naturally know which is the next pot to be shot. But if you *do* pick the wrong one, the boat will drag the right one out, no matter where it is, and likely as not you'll have a dozen pots overboard before you can stop.'

'Aye. And lucky if it's only pots that go overboard,' shouted John, without glancing from his task.

'Aye,' Henry agreed. 'It's not so long ago that a Burnharbour boat was shooting in weather like this, and the chap who was doing what Marney is now, got hold of the wrong pot. The right one was under his foot, and it shot up, and the tow got round his leg, and before he knew what had happened he was overboard, and being dragged down underneath by the tow. He was a cool sort of chap, however, and one that had done a lot of swimming and diving, as a lad. I don't know how many prizes he'd won at Burnharbour Regatta. He didn't lose his wits. The tow was still fast round his leg, and was dragging him deeper all the time, but he kept his mouth closed, and he managed to get his knife out and he'd started hacking at the tow before they'd got the boat stopped, and hauled him to the top. He wanted his mates to go on fishing. But the tow had made a mess of his leg, torn it right through his trousers, and they had to rush him ashore and get him to a doctor. He was all right again in a week.'

I knew of the absolute veracity of this seemingly incredible incident, but it was not until now, as I watched Marney bending over the slush-covered thwarts to pick up the next pot, that I fully realized its horror. And it was with something more than an ordinary thrill that I heard

Henry remark:

'Aye. There'll be none of that when we're shooting those shut-up pots of yours. It'll be a safer job altogether.'

I was glad to see the last pot safely shot. But there were still two other fleets to haul and shoot, and all the time the weather was becoming worse. The last sign of land had long since disappeared in the veil of driving snow. It seemed miraculous that Henry should know the exact position of the buoys of the second fleet. The visibility was so poor that I did not see the first of them until we were almost on top of it. The first fleet had taken about an hour to haul and shoot. But now, in addition to the increased power of the wind and sea, the tide had turned and was against us. Half a dozen pots had been hauled and cleaned and stowed, when John sounded the first note of protest.

'What about that third fleet, father?' he said. 'Hadn't we better give it a miss? It's going to be a gale before it's done with, and it's ten to one it's breaking now across the Landing.'

Henry made no audible answer: but Marney quickly retorted:

'Garn, of course we're going to haul it. It's a long way from being a gale yet. It will be as smooth as a mill pond soon as we get in the lee of Low Batts. That third fleet's on better ground than either of these. There'll be twice as many crabs in it, and I bet crabs will be fetching a damned good price, too. Besides, we're going to put the new pot in that fleet. You know we were one short in it. Shut up about going home. I want to see us get so many crabs that Luke and Tindal will have to help us up with them, same as we had to help them with their fish yesterday.'

I was wet now, in addition to being cold. My benumbed hands were sore with the rough netting of the pots, and my limbs were exhausted with the sheer effort of keeping my balance when I lifted the pots and stowed them. I longed for the feel of unmoving land under my feet again. I was haunted by the thought of shelter, of a fire, of dry clothes, of hot food and drink. Yet there was something infectious in Marney's enthusiasm. It was like hearing a battlecry. We were fighting the sea. We had won something. We would win more. I wished exultantly to see the cribs full. I wished us to beat the Fosdycks, and I wished to see my own pot shot, and the first real test of it begun.

We did slightly better with that second fleet. We shot it; and John made no further protest, as his father turned the boat again for the as yet invisible buoys of the third.

Marney in some miraculous fashion had succeeded in lighting a fag. He was smiling as he swayed to and fro, in sympathy with the pitching and rolling of the boat. But all the time he was looking ahead for the buoys.

'If we do as well with this fleet, as we've done with the others, it'll be the best day we've had this winter,' he said. 'That's the best of our pots. They're as good for crabs as they are for lobsters. We ought to make at least five quid for this morning's work. . . . There's a buoy, father,' he suddenly shouted, 'over on the starboard bow. I can see only one though.'

Henry steered towards the buoy. Not until we neared it, however, did he comment on the fact that the second buoy was still invisible; and all three meanwhile had kept an urgent look-out for it.

'It's a queer thing,' he said, 'it ought to be showing.'

'It ought to be showing, if it was there,' was John's quickly pessimistic interpretation of its non-appearance. 'But it *isn't* there. Summat's happened. I shouldn't be surprised if a bloody trawler's cut it adrift. Aye, and taken half the fleet with it.'

No one made any comment on this doleful diagnosis.

Marney gaffed the buoy, and this time as soon as the boat swung round and Henry lifted the tow over the derrick, I got a hold on the tow myself, and soon the four of us were hauling. I had no mitts. My hands were soft, and the palms of them had blisters which the rope tore, and the sea water burnt like acid. It was still snowing. Sea after sea smashed under the coble stern and the wind whipped the spray in our faces, so that it felt like hail. But I did not care. The feel of that rope gave me a sense of personal conflict with the sea. It roused me to a fighting fury.

We won the anchor and the first pot, with fifteen crabs in it. I prepared to stow it, but Marney signed to me to continue hauling, and when it was cleaned he rushed forrard and stowed it himself, returning just in time to lift in the second with the biggest catch of a score. He made no comment. Obviously something disastrous had happened to the fleet, for the next pot to come in had one of its bows smashed and several meshes of its net torn. The weather had not been bad enough to cause the pots to move. Buoys are too well secured for them to be lost except by some such accident as John had diagnosed. I had heard of entire fleets being dragged away by trawlers fishing inside the three-mile limit. Was John right? If so, how many pots had gone?

Marney made rough repairs to the pot. We hauled in silence. Marney had been right about this fleet being shot on better ground, for in succession we had three pots each with a score, and there was none with less than a dozen. But every pot showed signs of having been dragged along the bottom. All were more or less damaged, their hazels strained, their netting scrubbed. And the true loss had still to be known. How many had gone completely? A single lost pot could not be compensated by the catch in crabs of half a dozen, and it was the pots themselves that made the harvest now. We had hauled twenty when the first definite indication of the extent of the disaster came. The tow refused to give another foot. Marney took my place at it. I took hold behind him. We heaved with all our might, let go, and then heaved again. Nothing happened except that at the moment of our maximum exertion which forced the stern low into the water, a short sea broke clean into the boat.

Marney left go and rushed to the bilge pump. There was a risk of water getting at the engine. We hung on while he pumped. Then we tried again, and went on trying for nearly ten minutes. Then as we made one sudden united heave, the tow gave. I fell backwards, with Marney on top of me, and John on top of Marney, and Henry saving himself by hanging on to the derrick. We got to our feet again, and I seized the tow. But I saw at once that there was no longer work for the four of us. Henry and John hauled. Almost immediately a pot appeared, damaged, but full of crabs, and Marney seized it and they went on hauling. Their speed showed how little was left to haul. Another pot appeared. Henry left go and John coiled in the remainder of the tow until he came to a frayed and eloquently empty end, which he held up and gazed at ruefully as one might gaze at some relic of a killed pet.

'I thought as much,' he said in his gloomiest voice. 'A bloody trawler must have caught that other buoy and dragged the whole fleet along until a pot fouled, and then dragged the rest of them to God knows where. How many have we lost?'

'We've got twenty-one,' Marney answered. 'There was one short in this fleet, remember. That makes eight. It might have been ten, anyway.'

'Eight brand new pots! That's going to give the Fosdycks something to laugh at, isn't it, even if they *have* got to help us up with our crabs. And those we've got will all want mending soon. Eight pots are worth a damned sight more than all we've caught to-day.'

'The Fosdycks won't know we've lost them,' Marney retorted, 'unless you go blabbing about it all over the place. Come on,' he added, as he mended a torn mesh in the last pot. 'Let's get these shot again. It's no use crying over spilt milk. We've got a spare buoy and anchor. And weve got another pot, too, so we'll only be seven short. And I reckon that patent pot will be worth at least three of those we've lost.'

I did not take this last remark seriously. It was only a typical effort of Marney's to put a more cheerful aspect on what had occurred. But I felt immensely thrilled to think that my pot was to step as it were at once from the reserve to the front fighting line.

Henry, who had made no remark whatever upon the disaster, said suddenly:

'Start your engine, John.'

John primed the engine. And before we were under way again Marney had bent the 'strop' of my pot, mooring gear, and a buoy, to the frayed end of the tow. We turned into the weather. Marney heaved the buoy over. When it was trailing clear of the boat, he followed this with the anchor, and picking up my pot, threw it clear, and shouted after it:

'Good-bye, honey! It's up to you to fill yourself with crabs.'

The shooting continued. There were only twenty-one more pots to shoot, and soon there were only two pots left, those that were stowed for'ard in my original resting place. They were, as I had guessed, the most awkwardly placed of the fleet; for to get at them one had to kneel on a thwart and bend down, using both hands. The first of these Marney secured and cleared without difficulty; but as he bent over for the second, and the last of the fleet, the coble gave an unexpected lurch. His knees slipped. The pot was torn from his hands. It was held for a second by the edge of the thwart, then, with the full drag of the boat upon it, it cleared and took charge, bouncing end over end on the next thwart, straight for John, standing by the remaining coils of the tow. Had it struck him, it might have killed him. Had it fouled him most certainly it would have dragged him over. And possibly the realization of his peril prompted that swift reflexive act which conscious thought would have made too late. He let go of the tow. He met the charging pot with his hands outstretched, and without attempting to arrest its progress, he deflected it to the gunwale. It caught the hauling derrick. It cracked it off like a carrot, and crashed into the sea. And then, with incredible speed, John seized the tow again, whipped it overboard, let the anchor go and then the buoy.

Henry put the helm hard over. The coble dipped into the trough of a sea, and reared up on the slanting crest of another, like a horse startled by the explosion of a gun. And it was not until we were moving at full steam towards the invisible land, that anyone referred to what had happened; and it was John who spoke.

He pointed to the stump of the derrick.

'God,' he said, almost plaintively. 'That shows you what force there was on that pot, doesn't it? It might easily have killed me. Who's got a fag?'

3

The north-east breeze became a gale before night, and it continued with varying intensity for the whole of that week, with intermittent falls of snow, and a temperature, which, even during the occasional periods of bright sunshine, never rose above freezing point. The whole bay from High Batts to Low Batts was white with breakers. The tides were spring, and at high water giant waves smashed over the sea wall, and the wash of them went so far up the Dock that the cobles had to be moved half way up the Road for safety. Even so the snow lying in the Dock was only changed to slush, which froze rapidly as soon as the tide went down again.

I lay awake every night, listening to the noise of the sea, and thinking of the pots we had shot, and particularly of my own, lying on the bed of the gale-swept bay. As a boy that invisible territory whose western boundaries are the oar-weed banks that mark the scaur ends of a low spring tide, had excited my most glamorous dreams. I remembered how, having been told in a Sunday School lesson that one had only to pray earnestly for a thing to have that thing granted, I had prayed earnestly to God that night, that I might be given the power to stay under water as long as I liked, so that I might be able to explore the whole bed of Bramblewick Bay. I had imagined myself equipped with this divinely granted power, to which I prayed might be granted the power to defend myself against sharks, octopuses and giant conger eels, walking into the sea from the scaur ends—to the horror and envy of the village patriots—and at once perceiving all manner of strange and fascinating things: fishes such as no fisherman had ever caught; monstrous sea-urchins and star-fish, anemones growing like flowers in a garden; and, more exciting still, sunken wrecks, including that of an Armada treasure ship, which a fisherman had told me was still lying not far from High Batts; from which I would fill my pockets full of gold coins to take home and astonish my mother. Fortunately before starting on this adventure next day, I had taken the precaution to test my expected gift, by seeing how long I could remain with my head immersed in a rock pool, a test which did not encourage me to make a more drastic experiment, and left me a cynical doubter in the efficacy of prayer, although it did not stop me dreaming of underwater exploration.

Thus in the darkness, with the sea-gale rattling my bedroom windows, and the noise of the sea so strong, I had only to keep my eyes closed to be transported to where my pot was lying, to imagine visually what was happening there. I had no qualms as to its safety. Bad weather, I knew from what the Lunns had told me, would do no harm to pots that were lying on muddy ground, once they were water-logged and of course anchored. And there was no chance in such weather of a steamer or a trawler fouling them, for all such craft were obliged to keep miles from the land. I imagined it only in connection with its virtues as a trap. I pictured it lying on the mud, with the cod-head Marney had fixed in it, making a phosphorescent glow in the dark, exuding those peculiar rays which to the sensory organs of shell-fish may be those of sight or scent, or even sound. I pictured a crab reacting to those rays; moving closer to the bait until it found its progress arrested by the netting, and crawling round the pot until it was in the outer orifice of one of the spouts, and then with its progress to the bait no longer baulked, crawling in and finally passing the inner orifice, which by the clever masking of the meshes, permitted no return. I put myself in the position of a crab, which at the same time was attracted by the bait of the nearest Lunn pot; and I imagined reasons why it should prefer to move not towards theirs but towards mine. The bait of mine, because of the more simple frame, would be less obviously inside a trap. The spouts of mine, because there were no lumps of ballast and their lashing in the way, provided an easier and quicker entry. If the tide was strong, my pot, because of its slender shape, would be less likely to vibrate than the bulky hazel pots. This in itself might give it a big fishing advantage.

I pictured my pot already swarming full of crabs, and was troubled by the thought that I had not made it bigger than the hazel pots, to accommodate its bigger catch. And, while I knew that lobsters were rare on that muddy ground where the pots were shot, I imagined a stray specimen striking the fleet, and moving inevitably towards mine, and, provided there was room for it, being trapped.

It was a long week. I had a letter to say that the District Inspector would carry out the final test as soon as he heard from me that the batch was ready. But there was nothing I could do in this matter until I received the frames from Leeds. The Lunns busied themselves making new pots to replace the ones that had been lost, and I helped them. To me, however, the hazel pot was obsolete, and it seemed a waste of time to make new ones. The continued storm filled me with a wild impatience.

During the week-end the wind backed to north-west, finally to west. A slight thaw set in. The wind died and freshened again from the south-west, bringing a heavy rain which completely ended the frost, and melted even the moorland snowdrifts in a few hours. The sea moderated, but not sufficiently to make the Landing Mouth navigable until the middle of the following week when there came a day of almost incredible calm.

We were away shortly before dawn, and we had with us eight new pots. There was no swell, no wind; the air was as mild as on a summer's day, yet dry and invigorating. The sun had risen by the time we reached the fishing grounds. It threw a lane of light over the polished sea, in which the pennants of the pot buoys were silhouetted like the sails of tiny becalmed ships. It was hard to realize that the last time we had seen those buoys was in a growing blizzard, with the coble pitching on end and ourselves nearly frozen. I was excited. This was the first practical fishing test of my invention. The Lunns were excited, too, but for a different reason. I had guessed from the minute we had met in the Dock what was in their minds. Provided it held, here was ideal lobster weather, and the first of the season. Even at Burnharbour very few boats were at present engaged with their pots. If we got a catch, we should strike a highly favourable market, and with crabs, too, in good demand after the spell of bad weather, there was every prospect of a record day.

'Are we going to take them all close in, father?' Marney remarked as we drew near the buoys. 'We could manage two fleets at once with the sea like this.'

'No,' said Henry. 'We'll leave that fleet that got messed up out here. It'll not be much use for lobsters with these new pots to go in it. But we'll take that patent pot in and give it a go. We'd better haul that fleet first, then we can keep the other two on board. That's its buoy, straight ahead.'

Like an eager yet shy performer at an amateur concert, I funked the two extremes for my appearance on the stage. I was glad that I was to be spared the suspense of watching eighty-two pots hauled before my own; yet as Marney gaffed the buoy, it was with relief that I recognized it as the first of the fleet, and not the one that marked the broken end.

It was still calm. The tides were neap and dead slack, and a third hand was unnecessary with the hauling. The anchor was up in less than five minutes, and then quickly came the first pot. I had frequently heard Marney refer to pots as 'filling themselves'. I had taken it merely as a conventional superlative, meaning a very good catch. But now I saw that it was an exact description. The pot which with some difficulty he lifted over on to the thwart, was literally full, so that the netting at each end was bulging, and there would have scarcely been room for another one. He did not attempt to take them out by hand. He opened the door, leaned the pot over the crib and shook it savagely, and he had scarcely got it re-baited than another was up, and this likewise was filled. He gave me the first one to stow, next to the batch of new ones which were baited and ready to be bent on to this fleet when it was re-shot. He was grinning again.

'I told you you'd have to go a long way to beat one of our pots, didn't I?' he cried as he shook the second lot out. 'Damn it, I believe they'd catch crabs even if they hadn't any bait. Crabs seem to like getting into them, just like kittens like getting into a basket. And they're good crabs, too. If we can get six kits of them, and three score of lobsters later on, it'll be a good day's work.'

I was glad that we had made such a promising start; yet, as I watched pot after pot come on board, and practically every one of them full, I could not avoid a certain envious fear. I had hoped and believed that from the first my own pot would prove itself superior in every way to the hazel ones, that its catch would be at least above the average. Obviously this could not happen now, even if it was full. The only possible way in which it could score would be for it to catch one or more lobsters, and this hope was strengthened when a pot came in containing in addition to its filling of crabs a small lobster with only one claw. Marney took it out respectfully and put it in a basket. I had counted the pots. This was the nineteenth. There were two more before my own and the end of the fleet. And the Lunns for the first time indicated that they, too, were mildly excited, for Henry remarked as he hauled:

'We ought to be getting to that patent pot soon. I wonder how it's fished?'

'Aye. I've been wondering that all week,' said John. 'Of course it hasn't had the same chance as ours, with ours having been fishing already.'

'I don't think that will make any difference myself,' said Marney. 'I reckon it will be full, same as the rest. It ought to be. I put a good bait in it. It's the one after the next,' he added as he lifted another full pot into the boat.

Henry and John continued hauling. By the time I had got that pot out of the way the next one had appeared. Once again it was a full one. But I did not wait to see

Marney clean it. I peered over the side at the rapidly ascending tow. The water was dirty. It had almost broken the surface, when Henry, without waiting for Marney, reached his hand down and swung it on board. He did not make any immediate remark. It was Marney who first gave verbal expression to our dismayed surprise.

'My God,' he muttered. 'Not even a crab!'

Apart from a number of whelks, the pot was empty.

I was dumbfounded. I did not in that moment seek for any explanation. I accepted it simply as a sign of complete failure. There was still bait in the pot. There was no obstruction in the spouts, the door was fastened so that nothing having got in could have escaped. The net was undamaged. The last hazel pot had been filled with crabs, and the distance that had separated them on the bottom was not more than sixty feet. Obviously there was something about my pot which instead of making it more attractive to crabs actually repelled them. And if it repelled crabs, it would with equal certainty repel lobsters.

We all continued to stare at it, and neither Henry's nor John's comments did anything to dispel the gloom of my thoughts. Henry was coiling in the buoy line.

'It's a queer thing,' he said slowly. 'A damned queer thing.'

'It completely beats me,' said John. 'I'd have backed it against any of ours.'

'Being a new pot couldn't have made all that difference,' Marney added. 'It isn't so tarry as ours; and everyone of ours had something in it, first haul.'

Henry pulled the buoy on board. Then he said curtly to Marney:

'Take it off, and get those other pots bent on,' and to John, 'Start your engine.'

My pot was left on the thwart. I looked at it, as one might look at a trusted friend discovered in an act of abysmal treachery; and I had a sudden impulse to seize it and throw it overboard, and be done with it for ever. But I was called forward by Marney to help him. We were under way again. Soon the shooting began, and I moved aft, to Henry. He was looking at the pot out of the tail of his eye while he watched the shooting.

'Aye,' he said, with what appeared to me to be an air of condolence. 'It's a queer thing. I could have understood it if there'd been only a few crabs in it, but for it to be completely empty like that, is what I don't understand. Not when there's so many crabs about. Mind, I've known it happen before. We've had pots that have had nowt in them haul after haul. And then they've suddenly started to fish.'

'We've had one that never *would* fish,' put in John. 'Don't you remember it, last year? The most it ever caught was a ninycock. We brought it ashore in the end.'

'Aye. It was one you made,' shouted Marney. 'And it had a lot of white wood in the bottom. I've heard it said many a time that any white paint on a pot will stop it fishing.'

'It may be the galvanizing that's frightened them. Or it may be the iron frame, rattling on the bottom.'

'Aye. But what about that first little pot? That pot had two lobsters in it straight away.'

'It's a queer thing, and no mistake,' Henry said again. 'It reminds me that when we first came to Bramblewick there was a gentleman who used to come off lobstering with us, in fine weather, just for pleasure. He thought our pots were clumsy affairs, and that they didn't fish as well as they ought to; and he set to one day, making a pot of his own. It was a queer looking affair, more like a chicken coop than a pot, and it had wire netting round it. But the main difference was it had no proper spouts. He reckoned lobsters and crabs could get out of our spouts if they had a mind to. So he made his with a little door at the end, with a weight on it like that in a rat trap, so that when anything trod on it, it gave way and then shut up again. We fished that pot alongside of ours for weeks, but it never caught as much as a whelk. Neither crabs nor lobster would go near it.'

'Crabs and lobsters are very queer things,' Marney said, as he flung the last pot of the fleet overboard, and Henry put the helm hard over for the buoys of the next. 'It's what I've said from the first. It's going to be a very great advantage having a pot that will shut up, but it's not going to be much use unless it fishes as well as ours. I've been wondering whether it's those side sticks that have anything to do with it. I've always said having no side sticks spoils the look of it anyway.'

I was feeling too unhappy to enter into an argument, or to try and defend my pot in any way. I felt worse when we started hauling the second fleet, and found that it had fished as well as the first.

I felt a growing hatred for each hazel pot as it came in, bursting with crabs. I felt like a parent at a school prize-giving, watching a procession of proud and honoured children marching with their prizes from the platform, while his own child has won nothing and is disgraced. We stowed that fleet, and immediately began the hauling of the third. It, too, had fished up to the standard of the first. By the time we had finished, both of the coble cribs were full, and a basket had to be used for the overflow. The coble itself was stacked so high with pots that John had barely room to use the handle of the engine; and I saw that had anything like a breeze started to blow, we would have been obliged to re-shoot at least one fleet, or risk capsizing. Here my invention would show to greatest advantage. Three fleets of shut-up pots would not account for more room than a dozen hazel pots. But this meant nothing now, I thought bitterly. The most important function of a lobster pot was to fish.

We moved at full speed shorewards. There was still no wind. The sea was calm and pale blue, like a sheltered lake. I thought that I had never seen the coast of the Bay look more beautiful with the sun shining full on its cliffs, and making exquisite tones of red and grey where last week all had been sombre. There was the intoxication of early spring in the air, but this, like alcohol, served only to accentuate my state of mind, to deepen my depression. The Lunns, however, had quickly recovered from any disappointment the failure of my pot might have caused them. They didn't mention the matter again. Even John was excessively cheerful.

'God,' he cried. 'It's a bit of luck getting a day like this. Lobsters ought to be as thick as crabs, close in.'

'Aye. And they ought to bring a damned good price,

too,' said Marney. 'We ought to make at least six quid to-day, with all these crabs, too. We ought to coin money. I bet the Fosdycks are wishing they'd got their pots in. I bet they'll do badly with cod, fine weather like this.'

The Fosdycks, who as usual had been the first to leave the shore this morning, were still 'lining', and we could see their boat at the south end of the Bay, moving slowly towards the village. They would be ashore long before we were. Unless they had a phenomenal catch, they would have the mortification of seeing the Lunns score another triumph over them. I was not going to share in that triumph. My one consolation was in the thought that no one but the Lunns could possibly know what had happened.

We steamed north of the village, close in to the foot of Low Batts. A flock of herring gulls flew out of the cliff protesting with wild screams at our intrusion. Marney flung the buoy of the last fleet we had hauled overboard; as soon as Henry gave the word, he and John began shooting along a course that was practically parallel with the cliff.

'This is about the best place for lobsters along the whole of the coast,' Henry remarked to me as he kept careful watch on the shooting. 'But it's the worst I know of to be caught by a north-easter. It doesn't take more than half an hour of a good blow to have all this broken water.'

'You couldn't get away with two fleets on board like this,' said John.

'No. One fleet's bad enough.'

'What about this patent pot,' said Marney. 'Shall I put

it with this fleet or with the other? We ought to give it another go.'

I had a suspicion that Henry had completely forgotten its existence, for he remarked, as though surprised:

'No. It had best go with the others now. We don't want to stop shooting while you bend it on. Put a good bait in it.'

The first fleet was shot. We steamed along the cliff foot for about a quarter of a mile, and meanwhile Marney, without saying a word, replaced the old bait in my pot with a new one, and then attached it to the other tow, not at the end this time, but well into the middle. I watched the operation without any quickening of my blood. I had no hope that it would do better with lobsters than with crabs. But when its turn came to be shot, I swore to myself that if it was hauled up empty again I would finally and absolutely abandon it. The last pot of the fleet crashed into the mirror-like sea. Marney heaved the bouy after it. We turned, and then he said:

'What are we going to do now, father? Are we going to have our dinners, and then come back or are we going to give them the once-over? I'd like to have a score of lobsters to lay out on the scaur when the Fosdycks come down to see how we've done.'

Henry grinned.

'We'll give 'em an hour. Stop your engine John, and we'll heave the anchor over.'

We remained at anchor for a full hour, and during the whole of that time not a single reference was made to my pot. We steamed back then to the first fleet, and started hauling at once. By giving them the 'once-over' Marney meant that instead of taking all the pots on board, and shooting them on fresh ground, they were merely hauled, and dropped back, a method of fishing possible only because of the extreme shallowness of the water and the absence of tide. I watched the operation with an enforced indifference. There was not, I told myself, anything very remarkable in the fact that the first pot had two full-size lobsters in it, and the next four pots one each. But when seven pots in succession were hauled completely empty, my spirits definitely rose. Even hazel pots it seemed were not infallible. But Marney was quick with a defensive explanation.

'Of course, they haven't had a chance, you know. I bet when we come back this afternoon, there'll not be a pot without at least one in it. Most of them will have two. You can't beat these pots of ours, either for crabs *or* lobsters. . . . Look at that!' he added suddenly, as he lifted a pot containing two fine lobsters into the boat. 'How's that for only an hour's fishing?'

It was, however, the last pot in that fleet to contain anything at all. The total bag was only thirteen. We steamed at once to the second fleet, and began hauling; and it was not until we had hauled twelve pots for a total of one ninycock that Marney referred to my own.

'We'll soon see now, if that patent pot will catch lobsters, or whether it just frightens them away. With all these empty it ought to have summat in it. If it's got nowt, I should like to try putting side sticks on it, just to see if it *does* make any difference.'

'Well, here it is,' said Henry. 'I can tell by the weight.

It's only half the weight of one of ours. It *would* make a difference, wouldn't it, hauling them in a tideway. We'd haul a fleet in half the time it takes to haul one of ours.'

'They'd be champion, if only they'd fish,' said John.

Marney leaned over the side. I did not look, as he took hold of it. I waited for his laconic 'nowt', and while he was silent, my first glance at the pot as he brought it on board confirmed my fear that again it had failed. For the lobster it contained was lying, not on the bottom, but perched like a frightened hen on the cord of one spout, and the crab was huddled in one corner, so that it was not until Marney opened the door that I saw it at all. But I might have known by the way in which all three Lunns were looking at it, that it had retrieved its character.

'A lobster *and* a crab!' shouted John. 'God—that shows there's nowt wrong with it.'

'A damned good lobster, too!' shouted Marney, taking it out and holding it up. 'One of the biggest yet, if not *the* biggest.'

'I knew it would fish,' said Henry. 'I knew it would fish as *well* as ours, and I still think it will fish better when it gets a chance. And it was like hauling nowt. I only wish we'd got three fleets of them ready for fishing.'

'When are you expecting those others to come?' said John respectfully, as he went on hauling. 'Why not order a lot more of them while you're at it. I bet that Fisheries chap will open his eyes when he sees them at work. . . . Here's another pot.'

My pot went back into the sea again. The next pot came in, empty. But I would not have minded if it had contained a dozen lobsters, and I felt a definite thrill when, after four more blanks, the last pot of the fleet came in with the record of three. I had proved that my own pot would fish at least as well as the hazel pot. With all its other advantages I need not ask it to do more. All that remained now was to prove this to the Fisheries Inspector, to demonstrate how a batch of them would be collapsed, erected, hauled and shot, under actual fishing conditions. Before this very lobster season was ended, the manufacture of my invention should have begun. No hazel pots would be required for the next season!

I was satisfied. I thought of my pot affectionately, as a hunter might think of a weapon that has served him well; and suddenly I abandoned myself to the intoxication of the day; of the sunshine, the colour of the sea and the sky and the cliffs, the red roofs of Bramblewick village gleaming through smoke that had the lustre of pearl; and I felt an intense friendliness towards my companions, towards their boat, their gear, towards their hazel lobster pots that were doomed in the name of Progress.

We were already steaming full speed for home. It was past twelve when we landed. The Fosdycks evidently had gone to dinner, for their coble was pulled close in to the scaur ready for launching up, but there was no sign of the men themselves. The tide was flowing, but very slowly. It was decided to leave the off-loading of the crabs until after dinner, and return to the pots and take them back to deep water for the night when this was done. As I got out, Henry picked up the lobster my pot had caught, tied its claws and gave it to me.

'You'd better take that for your tea!'

I took it, with the private reservation that at a suitable opportunity it would go the way of the first two; for now I felt even greater cause to be generous. I left the Lunns at the Slipway top, and hurried up to my cottage, carrying the lobster in my hand.

As I returned into my lane I observed Jane Allinson and Reub Brewster and his wife, standing together outside my door gazing eagerly at two large packages that lay there. They at once turned, and Jane and Reub both grinned at me in the familiar 'Bramblewick' way.

'Now then,' said Jane, 'have you been out fishing, with the Lunns? You've got a nice lobster in your hand.'

She and Reub continued to grin; but their gaze shifted back to the two packages, which, wrapped most inadequately in thin sacking, torn in many places, obviously contained the pot frames from Leeds.

Mrs. Brewster spoke a little nervously.

'The railwaymen brought these things for you, from the nine o'clock train. I told them you weren't in, and they asked me to sign for them. I didn't know if I was acting right. They said they were lobster pots, and I thought they must be making a mistake. They don't look like lobster pots, *do* they?'

'Nay. They don't look like lobster pots to me,' Jane echoed. 'Lobster pots are altogether different. They're a daft lot, them railway chaps.'

Reub said nothing; but he was grinning, and I caught something in his eyes which symbolized for me all the old enmity, the suspicion, the ironic mockery of the Bramblewick born towards the foreigner. But for once I did not mind. It was no longer of paramount importance that my invention should remain a secret. It did not worry me that before night the whole of the village would know of these two packages, and what they contained. Like the Lunns I had feared, above all, that Bramblewick should be laughing at me. The lobster I held in my hand was like a charm against this. I acknowledged rightful ownership of the packages, and thanked Mrs. Brewster for signing for them. Then I opened my door, and heaved them inside.

4

The weather continued fine into next week. The Lunns were fishing from dawn till dark, bringing their three fleets of pots close in to the rock, after the first haul, taking them back to deep water, last thing, for fear the weather might suddenly change. It was harder work than in bad weather. During the day the fleets were hauled at least six times. They dare not risk leaving the coble at anchor over night. It had to be hauled to the Dock. The crabs and lobsters had to be carried to the warehouse for packing. The packing itself was a tedious business. They were all pretty well tired out by the end of the day, and there was little enough time for the netting of my fifteen pots before bed. John with his choir practices, and various intrigues associated with the organization of the Brass Band, absolved himself of the task by admitting that he was only a poor hand at netting; and he was always washed and dressed within an hour of hauling up; a state which by itself would have forbade him to touch fishing gear. Henry's sight was not too good at night, particularly after a day of bright sunshine. He helped, but the main task of preparing the pots for the final test, devolved on Marney, and as Amy objected to him being away from home in the evening he had to do it in front of his own fireside.

At first we had the street door locked, and whenever Tom Fosdyck came, Marney would push the pot he was working on under the sofa, before letting him in. But this became too nerve-racking for all of us, and in the end it was decided that Tom should be the first real 'Bramblewicker' to see a completed shut-up pot. We chose for the occasion a night near the end of the week, when he rattled at the street door just as we had finished supper, a most unusual time for him to call, and to Marney a clear indication that he was dying to find out what we were up to. There was a finished pot on the hearth rug. Marney quickly collapsed it and hid it under the table. Then he let Tom in, and locked the door behind him. Tom came over to the fireside, lit his pipe, and reached his legs out comfortably to the fire; all this without saying a word to anybody. Marney, too, was silent, while he finished leisurely lighting a fag. Then with a wink at me he reached under the table for the pot, and put it across his knees.

'I'm damned if I remember if I put a bait-string in this one. Shall I open it up and see?'

Tom's eyes had lit up, but apart from this he gave no

sign of interest. He continued to puff at his pipe.

Marney laid hold of the erecting bar, and gave me another wink as he said:

'Have you ever seen a shut-up pot, Tom?'

Tom grinned faintly.

'Aye. We had plenty of shut-up pots, last year. The whole bloody lot of them shut up in that first gale.'

'Aye. But have you ever seen one that you could shut up and then open again like an umbrella?'

'No,' Tom answered stolidly.

'I bet you've heard of one, though,' put in Amy. 'You needn't try to be so innocent.'

'You hear *all* sorts.'

'I bet you guessed why our front door had been locked every night this week,' said Marney.

'I knew there was summat up.'

'I bet you heard all about those two bundles that came from the station the other day,' Amy pursued.

Tom's equanimity was not disturbed by this bombardment.

'Aye. Jane Allinson asked me if I'd ever seen a lobster pot made of iron, and she said she'd seen some, only she didn't believe they were lobster pots at all.'

'I bet your Uncle Luke and your Uncle Tindal have had summat to say about patent pots this past week or so.'

Tom did not answer this, which came perilously near a breach of that peculiar etiquette honoured by both Lunns and Fosdycks, and Marney quickly added:

'Aye. You do hear *all* sorts in Bramblewick, but it's very rare you hear the truth. I bet there's a lot of folks have been laughing up their sleeves about this patent pot, and saying it's all daftness. But there's no one here has seen one yet except us and father and our John. . . . Now you'll admit straight away that a pot that will shut up and open again is going to be very useful to chaps like us.'

'Aye. It would be all right if you were caught in bad weather, close in.'

I recognized a familiar irony in Tom's voice, but whether he did or not, Marney went on:

'And you'll admit that a pot which weighs half as much as yours or ours would be easier to haul in a tideway.'

'Aye. That stands to reason.'

'And you'll admit that a pot that won't smash in a swell is worth more than a hazel pot.'

'Aye.'

'Then here it is!' said Marney, laying the pot on the floor. 'Here it is shut up . . . and here it is open.'

He erected the pot and looked at Tom Fosdyck, and I wondered if he caught that quick gleam in the Bramblewick man's eyes that I caught; that fleeting expression of an ancient enmity which even the doglike devotion he had for Marney could not repress. He made no remark whatever. He made no effort to examine the thing more closely, but remained puffing at his pipe, and with just a suspicion of a grin on his face.

'I reckon myself that this pot is worth a dozen hazel pots.' Marney went on, in a way that reminded me grimly of my interview with the Birmingham works manager. *'You* had a lot of pots smashed up last year.

You'll have a lot smashed up this year. Like us, you'll be lucky if you end up the season with more than half a fleet left. And why? Just because you can't take all your pots on board when you want to rush them out to deep water when the weather comes on bad. That's chiefly what a shut-up pot's for. But this pot's got more to it than that. Being made nearly all of iron, it doesn't want any extra ballast. Being made of iron, it's six times as strong as hazels, so that even if it does get caught, it will take no harm. And as for fishing—God, the first time we tried, it was only a little model, and we put it down the Landing one night, and it had two lobsters in it next morning. We shot a full-sized one before that gale came on. It had filled itself with crabs when we hauled it. Damn it—you couldn't have forced another crab into it, it was that full. When we gave them the once-over close in, after only an hour's fishing, it had caught a lobster and a crab, and the next time we hauled it had two lobsters. I've lost count of what its caught since then.'

This was not true, any more than the filling of crabs, for my pot had been empty the second haul (when the total for the two fleets had been only seven) and I had decided then to bring it ashore, so that it might be added to my own fleet when this was ready. Yet I made no protest at Marney's exaggeration. I was as anxious as he was to impress Tom Fosdyck. Tom, however, remained completely unimpressed. He continued to puff at his pipe. There was a long silence. Then Marney said:

'Well, what do you think of it—honest?'

Tom grinned.

'It's all right,' he said slowly. 'It's all right.'

'Do you think it's a good idea?'

'Aye. The idea's all right.'

'Haven't you got anything else to say but "all right," "all right," every time?' put in Amy, tartly. 'You sound like a parrot.'

'I bet you, and your Uncle Luke, and your Uncle Tindal would like to have three fleets of them, instead of hazel pots,' Marney pursued. 'Think how you'd save your backs when you were hauling in a tideway, if nowt else.'

'Aye,' Tom answered. 'They'd be all right for that. But I reckon *they'd* not want to bother using things like those.'

'Why?' Marney demanded quickly.

'Why?' Amy repeated.

Tom grinned.

'Because they're used to fishing with t'other sort,' he answered. 'They've got the habit of them. They've fished with hazel pots all their lives, and they know where they are with a hazel pot. They'd not change now for a pot that caught a dozen lobsters for certain every time it was shot.'

'Aye. But *you're* different, aren't you? *You'd* rather have summat that makes more brass, and saves half your work, or do *you* stick to hazel pots?'

Tom grinned again.

'Hazel pots are all right,' he answered. 'They're all right.'

Marney gave a snort of disgust.

'Garn!' he cried. 'What's wrong with you is that you're too bloody old fashioned. You and your Uncle Luke and your Uncle Tindal ought to be running about naked, with brass rings through your ears and strings of beads round your bellies. You ought to have bows and arrows and a canoe instead of a coble. You're no better than a lot of bloody savages. It'll serve you right if you do have your living taken away from you, by those who have sense enough to keep up to date.'

I was not unduly upset to learn the Fosdycks' attitude towards my invention. I had never strongly expected that it would be otherwise than unfavourable. There would be many of the older fishermen who would think the same. Yet these men in a few years must inevitably retire from the sea. It was to the younger, more vigorous generation that it would appeal, men like Henry Lunn, who was still on the right side of sixty—particularly the men of Marney's generation. As for Tom himself he typified the end of a dying family. Neither Luke nor Tindal had children. Tom's heart had never been in fishing. He had taken to it only as a line of least resistance when he had lost his job at sea. And he was unmarried. He did not strike one as the sort of man who would marry and beget children. In this immense revival of the fishing industry that my invention would start, it was inevitable that a certain number of men should suffer as the hand weavers had suffered, when they had fought the steam loom. I was sorry for Luke and Tindal. The Lunns had already beaten them with their motor coble. My pots spelt for them complete economic defeat. Yet clearly the remedy would be in their own hands. They must move with the tide or be left behind. More tragic things than this had happened in the name of Progress!

*   *   *

I had received a letter from Mr. X. He was very pleased that I had been able to get the pots manufactured so cheaply, that the fleet would so soon be ready for the final test, and that the first trial of the single pot had been so satisfactory. He had discussed the whole proposition with several prominent persons, and he felt confident that if the Government report was satisfactory, there would not be much difficulty in securing the necessary financial backing to get the thing going. I had also received a further letter from the Fisheries inspector, saying that owing to other official engagements he might not be able to conduct the test for a fortnight. While I regretted the delay, it was not without its advantages. I was convinced that the failure of the first haul was due entirely to the pot being new. We decided that we should take the fleet to sea as soon as it was finished, so that it would be thoroughly seasoned by the date of the test. Henry suggested that it should go into the fleet that had been damaged, so that the 'scrubbed' pots might be brought ashore for repair. Only two pots remained to be netted by Saturday night. Marney would have liked to have finished them on Sunday, but Amy objected. She was not 'religious', but she was 'respectable', and it was not respectable to do anything like that on Sunday. We postponed the shooting until Tuesday, therefore, which would give us a week before the provisional date for the test.

I did not go to sea on Monday. Just after dinner I received a telegram from the Inspector, to say that he would arrive at Bramblewick by motor at five on Tuesday morning, and would I delay the Lunn's departure for the fishing grounds until then. I was embarrassed. I thought at first of wiring to say that I could not make the necessary arrangements. On second thoughts, however, I saw that it would be unwise to ask for a postponement. The weather could not possibly remain fair much longer. We need not trouble about the two unfinished pots. We could shoot the rest of them to-day, and while it was not giving them a fair fishing chance, the inspector would take this into consideration.

The Lunns were ashore. I rushed round to the warehouse and found the three of them cutting up bait for the afternoon's fishing. I told them my news, which, now that I had adjusted my mind to the changed plan, seemed exciting. No one, however, appeared to share my excitement. No one, in fact, spoke until I asked Henry direct if they were returning to sea at once, and if we could take the new pots. Then John gave me the first clue to what was in their minds.

'Eh!' he said. 'You don't want to take those patent pots down to the coble in broad daylight, do you, for everyone to see?'

I said that I was not concerned any more with keeping the secret of the pot. Any way, Tom Fosdyck had already seen it. But it was not this that disturbed him or the others, for he went on:

'There'll be dozens of folks in the Dock and on the Slipway Top on a fine afternoon like this. We'd have to walk right past them.'

'Luke and Tindal were both there when I came up, just now,' put in Marney. 'We'd have half Bramblewick out to look at us by the time we'd got the second lot carried down.'

'Aye. And laughing at us,' John went on. 'You know what an ignorant lot they are. *I'm* not going to march past them carrying patent pots, and have them all grinning and making sly remarks.'

'The best time to take those pots to sea is when we first go off in the morning,' said Marney. 'It's almost dark then, and there's no one about.'

'Aye,' Henry agreed. 'Or we could take them down and stow them in the coble to-night. No one would ever know we'd got them.'

I was too sensitive myself to the staring of the Bramblewick gossipers not to understand, and, to a certain extent sympathize with the Lunns; but I felt that too much depended on the pots getting at least a night's seasoning to let this stand in the way. I asked Henry again if they were going to sea soon.

'Aye. We'll be off as soon as we get this bait cut.'

'Well,' I said, 'if no one else will help to carry them down, I'll do it myself.'

'There's no need for you to do that,' Henry answered quickly, but with obvious reluctance. 'I'm not afraid of walking past the Fosdycks with those patent pots. They might laugh now, but they'll not laugh when we've had them fishing a bit. Have you got them over where you're living? We could put them on a hand-barrow, and cover them with an oilskin, and carry them all down in one go. I'm not afraid of the Fosdycks laughing at us.'

'Neither am I,' said Marney, 'if it comes to that, I'd walk down the Slipway with a patent pot in each hand, one of them open and the other shut up. And I shouldn't

257

care if all Bramblewick was there!'

'God—*I* would!' said John. 'I'd as soon walk into chapel without my trousers on. And I tell you, *you'd* think twice about it when you saw them all staring and grinning. I reckon we'd best do what father said, and take them down to the coble to-night. That Fishery chap can't expect to have everything arranged for him at a minute's notice, particularly as he said he wasn't coming for another week.'

I observed that this was not without its effect on Marney, and I said hastily:

'Aye. But we'd look damned silly all the same if they didn't catch a single crab or lobster, and the Inspector had to report it. He'd think there was something wrong with them; either the frame or the net.' I moved to the door. 'Don't worry. I'll have them down to the coble by the time you're ready.'

Marney put down his knife and wiped his hands on his trousers seat.

'I'll come with you,' he muttered, without enthusiasm. 'Wait a bit. I'll get the handbarrow, and a sack to shove over them.'

He did not speak once as we hurried over to my cottage. We stepped into the washhouse, and Marney himself carefully closed the door. The thirteen finished pots, with the first one we had tested, stood in a neat pile in one corner, all collapsed, and taking up no more room than four hazel pots. But Marney made no comment upon this—to me—gratifying sight. His nerves were keyed up, as though he were engaged on some unlawful business. He handled the pots as though we were stealing them, and now and again he stopped to listen. He spoke in tense undertones.

'We can carry the whole lot in one go. We'll cover them with the sack, then we'll wait until the street's clear . . . Listen. There's someone coming now. It's Jane Allinson. Damn it—there's Mrs. Brewster opening her door.'

There were footsteps on the cobbles outside. Marney paused in the act of putting the last pot on the barrow. We heard Jane, evidently addressing Mrs. Brewster:

'Now then. Are you just off to do some shopping? It still keeps fine, *doesn't* it?'

And Mrs. Brewster's response:

'Aye. It's good drying weather. Washing's dry almost as soon as you hang it out.'

We listened to footsteps receding in both directions. Then Marney hurriedly put the sack over the pile, fastened it with rope, and said:

'Now's our chance. That old devil will be back from the drying ground if we don't look sharp. I'm glad it's not Saturday. The kids will be at school, anyway.'

We made our way down towards the Dock, carrying without undue physical exertion, fourteen lobster pots; and I drew Marney's attention to the fact that we were performing in a single journey what would have needed at least four journeys with the old fashioned pots. But he said nothing but a laconic:

'Aye.'

We reached the Dock. Marney had allowed me to take the leading place at the barrow; and I saw as soon as we reached the Slipway top, that a number of men were standing there with their backsides against the breakwater wall; and among them were Luke and Tindal Fosdyck. This had been one of the favourite waiting places for the village patriots during the earlier days of my childhood; for it commanded both routes to the beach. One never knew, until one had reached the Slipway top, whether they were there or not; but if they were, there was no retreat. One had to slink past, eyes to the front, like a discreet dog doing its best to avoid a bigger one, pretending to be peacefully unaware of its existence, without, however, daring to suggest fear; and I remembered more than one occasion when my courage had failed under the ordeal, and I had taken to my heels with the whole pack of them after me.

The men who had been talking, stopped as we drew near. There were two elderly and decrepit Down-Bank ex-skippers, the village road sweeper, a retired carpenter, and two unemployed youths, in addition to Luke and Tindal. But I looked only at the Fosdycks, both of whom were grinning. Marney started to whistle a popular song. We were almost abreast. And then, to my amazement, he suddenly cried to me to stop, and obliged me to do so, by lowering his end of the barrow. We lowered it to the ground immediately in front of the staring men. I looked round. Marney's face was flushed. He was grinning, however; and, staring directly at Luke Fosdyck, he said:

'Now, Luke. We're just going to shoot some of those patent pots you've heard so much about. Would you like to have a look at one?'

It was the first time in my life I had seen Luke Fosdyck exhibit signs of nervousness. Despite his tan, he visibly blushed. His eyes shifted, and he muttered almost inaudibly:

'Aye. I'd like to have a look at one, if you've got one there.'

Marney whipped off the sacking.

'There's not *one* here, but fourteen,' he said. 'I reckon you couldn't carry fourteen ordinary pots on a hand-barrow, *could* you?'

Marney was the only person grinning now.

He took hold of the topmost pot.

'That's what they're like when they're shut up,' he said. . . . 'And this is what they're like when they're open.'

He opened the pot. There was a vague noise of astonishment from the rest of the spectators, but neither of the Fosdycks made any audible remark. Marney waited a minute. Then, closing the pot again he said:

'I thought maybe you'd like to see them. We're taking them out to put them instead of some we got scrubbed. They're handy things, aren't they? They only weigh about a quarter of what ours do, and yet they sink quicker. And fish! God—ours are nowhere alongside them. I wish we had three fleets of them. What do you chaps think of them?'

He put the sacking back and we bent down to the handles of the barrow. We lifted it up, and it was not until then that Luke Fosdyck answered that question:

'They're all right,' he said. 'They're handy, and no mistake. Four pots on a barrow are a load for us. . . . But *I* wouldn't use them.'

'Nay. *I* wouldn't, either,' said Tindal.

'Why?' said Marney sweetly.

'Coz they'll be like all these other new-fangled things,' Luke answered. 'They'll catch on for a time, and then you'll never hear another word about them. Hazel pots are good eough for *me.*'

'*And* for me,' muttered Tindal.

They both grinned; and suddenly I had a fierce desire to drop the barrow, and take to my heels. But Marney seemed quite encouraged by his own brave deed.

'Well,' he remarked with serene irony. 'Things *do* change you know. I bet when you were a kid in Bramblewick, folks had never heard of a water closet. Now there's scarcely a house that hasn't got one. And you'll have to admit they're a very great convenience.'

The barrow jerked as he took a step forward. We fell into stride down the Slipway to the beach and the Landing where, at half tide, the motor coble was just awash, with Henry and John already in it, discreetly preparing for departure.

'God!' Marney cried, with unrestrained enthusiasm. 'You wouldn't think that we were carrying fourteen pots, all in one go, would you? Let them laugh! That's what I say, let them laugh! It only shows their ignorance. They'll laugh the other side of their faces when we start fishing with three fleets of shut-up pots. . . . I'm glad we brought them down like this, aren't you, and laid them right at their feet? We'll show that Fishery chap what we can do with them to-morrow. I'm going to try and persuade father to leave them close in all night, in amongst the lobsters.'

5

I had met the Fisheries Inspector on the occasion of the first examination of the pot, and I had liked him. He was a retired Naval officer, and his position was, I understood, virtually an honorary one; his duties being to report on landings of fish, complaints of illegal trawling, destruction of gear by steamboats, the silting up of harbours, and such matters of interest both to the Fisheries Department and to the fishermen themselves. He had a breezy, genial manner, and a sense of humour. I had no doubt, however, that he had a serious conception of his responsibilities, and that this final test would be thorough, and his report frank. During the war—he had told me—it had been his duty to make practical tests of various types of inventions relating to mines, submarine nets, and anti-mine and U-boat devices. So many of them worked admirably in theory, but failed when submitted to the rigorous conditions of the sea and weather.

He arrived in the Dock to the minute, having left his car on the Bank Top. Both cobles had been launched, and the Fosdycks had already put to sea, so that we were saved the embarrassment of their curiosity. It was another fine, calm morning, with just a light westerly wind. During the last few days the price of crabs had fallen so low that they were no longer worth the cost of packing and carriage to market. With lobsters in still good demand, and the weather giving every promise of remaining calm, Henry had yielded to Marney's persuasion to leave all three fleets of pots close in along Low Batts. Clearing the Landing Posts we steamed in that direction.

The Inspector was at home in a coble; and at home with the Lunns. He had made Henry's acquaintance during the war, when, as skipper of the deep-sea motor boat, Henry had earned a reputation along the coast for his contempt of mine-fields and enemy submarines; and when he had been somewhat of a thorn in the side of the naval authorities. They chatted about those adventurous days: they went on to discuss fishing in general, the failure of the winter cod fishing, the depletion of the old fishing grounds by trawlers, marketing conditions, cost of gear, and loss of gear; but it was not until the pot buoys were visible that their conversation came near to touching the main object of our expedition.

'Are you fishing all your pots close in?' the Inspector remarked.

'Aye. But this is the first time we've risked it.' Henry answered. 'And I got out of bed twice during the night to see what the weather was like. I should think more pots have been smashed up along this bit of cliff, than in any other spot along the whole coast. And yet it's one of the best for lobsters. The sea grows so quick just here when the wind gets east of north. It doesn't give you any time to haul and get your pots into deep water.'

'I suppose it was that that first gave you the idea of

using collapsible pots, eh?'

'Aye. It came to me one day when we nearly capsized trying to take two fleets at once. Thinks I, if only all these pots could be shut up, we wouldn't know we'd got them on board, except for ballast. But it took a better brain than mine to think out how it could be done.'

'Aye,' said John, grinning in my direction, yet talking at the Inspector. 'It was all a bit of luck how it came to be done at all, wasn't it? It was just luck that I happened to go round to your spot to talk about a scheme some of us have for starting a brass band. We're organizing it now as a matter of fact and I think we shall get it going this summer, if we can get enough subscriptions in. . . . Well, I happened to mention quite casually, that father was trying to think out how he could make a "shut-up" pot. And the next time I saw you, you'd got one made hadn't you? It was only a small one, but it caught two lobsters.'

'He brought the frame round to me,' said Marney. 'I'll admit I laughed when he told me it was a model lobster pot. But it looked all right when we got it netted. At the same time I was surprised that it fished so well straight off. A new pot will catch crabs, if they're on the feed. But it's rare they will do anything with lobsters until they've been well soaked.'

'Aye,' said Henry, with meaning. 'It's a pity this lot wasn't shot a week ago. They've not had a fair chance.'

I had already taken the precaution to explain to the Inspector that the pots had been shot for the first time yesterday afternoon; and I was relieved to hear him say at once that of course he did not expect them to perform as if they had been seasoned. Personally he could think of no reason why they should not fish at least as well as the old type, although an old Burnharbour fisherman with whom he had discreetly discussed the use of iron pots, had told him that they were no use at all, as the rattle of them frightened lobsters away. This he thought was absurd.'

'Aye,' put in Marney. 'That's pure daftness.'

The Inspector agreed, and went on to say that what he particularly wished to see was whether the collapsing and erecting, that seemed so simple an operation ashore, could be done under actual fishing conditions, and particularly when the boat was travelling at ordinary speed. This, he presumed was the most important claim I made for the invention.

We reached the first buoy. At once there was a perceptible change in the Inspector's manner. He looked stern and official. I became uncomfortably nervous. Actually I did not value his opinion on the pot as much as Henry's. He was not after all a fisherman. But I was convinced that in the vague world of business and finance from which was to come the wherewithal for the organization of my factory, a favourable official report would carry overwhelming weight. I was convinced that my fate lay in the Inspector's 'yes' or 'no'. I was so nervous that I failed to notice whether it was the buoy of my fleet or of one of the others, and I had my first sense of relief when Marney lifted a hazel pot into the coble. It contained two lobsters.

The Inspector at first made no remark. Marney handed me the pot to stow. Another pot appeared. It also contained two lobsters, and the next had three. This was good fishing, with lobsters still averaging two shillings apiece, and the Inspector was obviously impressed, for when the next one appeared with two again he remarked:

'Well, there doesn't seem to be much wrong with *your* pots so far as fishing goes.'

All three Lunns grinned.

'Aye. They're not bad pots,' said Henry with quiet pride.

'I'll back them against any pot there is for fishing,' said John.

'They're as good for crabs as they are for lobsters,' said Marney.

'I believe all those Burnharbour boats are using this sort now,' Henry went on. 'When we first came here from Sledburgh, they were using the four-bowed pot same as the Fosdycks use now. They're nothing like so good as this sort.'

'If you ask me,' said Marney. 'That's the best thing about this patent pot. It's as near to our sort as it possibly can be without interfering with it shutting up. The chief difference is, of course, that it's got no sticks along the sides. That makes it look a bit queer, but it seems to make no difference as regards fishing. It will fish as well, if not better than these; and we'd prove it, if only they weren't brand new. It wouldn't surprise me a bit if they were all empty.'

There was not a pot in that fleet which did not contain at least one lobster. We re-shot it and went on to the next. I knew this time by the buoy, that my own were to be left to the last; and although Henry gave me no sign, I knew that he was deliberately doing this to keep them fishing as long as possible. I told myself that it was not of vital importance that they should fish well. There was a perfectly valid reason for their doing otherwise. But if they *did* contain lobsters, in spite of their newness, then it would be a distinct score, and the psychological effect would be immense. The second fleet was up to the average of the first. It was re-shot. We steamed towards the buoys of the third.

There was a complete silence while Marney got the buoy on board, and handed the two to Henry and John. Then Henry said:

'I'm damned if I remember whether the shut-up pots are at this end of the fleet or the other. . . . We put them in a fleet of ours that got cut in two by a trawler,' he explained to the Inspector. 'There's fourteen shut-up pots, and the rest are hazels.'

'They're at *this* end,' said John, who had taken first position at the tow. 'You could tell the difference if you were here. It's like hauling nowt after hauling our pots. . . . You take hold, mister,' he said to the Inspector. 'Feel the weight.'

The Inspector did so.

'They're very light,' he said. 'Are you sure you've got a pot off the bottom yet?'

For answer John took hold again, heaved in about a fathom, and shouted to Marney as the 'strop' of the first pot appeared. Marney bent over the gunwale.

'Here we are,' he said, doing his best to say it quite calmly. 'Only one. But it's a good 'un.'

He lifted the pot in, and laid it on the thwart in front of the Inspector, with a fine lobster flapping on its bottom. And I thought I had never heard a sweeter sound. I looked at Marney, and he winked at me. John was grinning. Henry's face, too, wore a confident smile as he turned and said to the Inspector:

'You ought to take that one back with you. First one you've seen caught in a shut-up pot.'

The Inspector smiled and thanked him, but he was examining the pot intently. Marney took out the lobster, re-baited it, then dramatically lifted the catch, collapsed the pot and laid it on the boat bottom by the engine box. He said nothing, and I was glad, for that practical demonstration did not need the emphasis of words. The pot was new, yet it had caught a lobster first 'shot'. It had collapsed with a mere touch of the hand. And the second pot came in with two lobsters, not so big as the first, but full size and marketable. . . . With the fourteenth pot the total catch of that fleet was twenty-five. The sixteen hazel pots increased it only by another score. None of these had more than two. Two were completely empty. Everyone of mine had caught at least a lobster.

The Inspector maintained his stern, official air; but I knew that he was satisfied. As we got under way again I saw him intently examining the pile, which reached no higher than the lid of the engine box; and then glancing at the others piled up forrard. It was a more dramatic demonstration of the advantages of my invention than if there had been no hazel pots on board. There remained nothing but to show him that they could be erected, and shot just as simply and safely as they had been hauled, and for that I knew I could rely on the Lunns.

'I don't want you to run any risks with them,' the

Inspector remarked as Marney lifted the buoy. 'I know what an awkward thing shooting is, under steam, and you've had no practice with this new gear. Do it at half-speed, if you like.'

'We can manage them all right,' said Marney. 'They're twice as easy to get at as ours. . . . Say when, father.'

Father gave the sign for the buoy to go over. There was no anchor. As soon as the tow was trailing clear, Marney took the topmost pot of the pile, erected it and heaved it over. Before its strop had tightened he had the next one erect and ready. . . . The shooting went on without a hitch, and at full steam. Not once had John to touch the engine throttle. There was no moving about the boat, climbing over slippery thwarts, no need to think out which pot came next, no possibility whatever of shooting a pot out of turn. The erecting process was almost automatic. The whole business was quick, simple, safe, eminently practical; and this again became more obvious by comparison when the last of my pots went over, and Marney had to start climbing over the thwarts for the heavy, unwieldy hazel pots. And this was fine, calm weather. I thought of that winter's morning when the last pot was torn from Marney's hands and took charge and nearly split John's head open; and an immense satisfaction possessed me. My invention had been given a practical test by practical men. It had proved its merits magnificently. I abandoned myself again to the intoxication of the sea, and the sunshine and the landward view, and the rhythm of the coble as, with the shooting done, we steamed homewards on the slow swell of the flood tide. . . .

I saw the quick end of personal poverty: I saw my ideal factory, in busy existence. I saw the Lunns established as the well-paid, practical demonstrators of shut-up pots; the British in-shore fishing industry revived, rationalized, expanded, the start of a lobster and crab cannery which would be the nucleus of a tremendous industry. I saw how the whole thing might be united into a great co-operative organization, embracing the manufacture of the pot, the ownership of boats, the actual fishing, the sale and distribution and canning of the catch. It might be called the BRITISH IN-SHORE FISHERIES COMPANY. There would be fleets of express motor cars that would collect the catch every day from the ports, and take it to the distribution centre. Here would be boiling tanks, where under the most scrupulously hygienic condition, lobsters and crabs would be cooked, packed, and dispatched to inland towns. Each one would be stamped or bear the special symbol of the COMPANY, which would be a guarantee that it had been caught, and cooked within a certain number of hours. The COMPANY might own its own shops, restaurants, quick-lunch bars. It might employ fleets of bicycle vans by which its products might be delivered direct to the consumer. The youths in charge of them would wear a special uniform, with caps bearing the symbol of the COMPANY. This symbol might be a design of a lobster in a lifebuoy bearing the initials B.I.F.CO., and BIFCO as a name would become a household word throughout the land, as well-known as BOVRIL.

Yet while I indulged in this pleasant dream, my mind

was already engaged formulating a plan of action. The Inspector's report would have to be made to headquarters, and would probably pass through many official hands before it was available. Much valuable time would be lost if we waited until then. Time would be lost, too, if I continued to exchange views with Mr. X merely by writing. It was my obvious duty to go up to London without delay, to take one of the pots with me, to explain personally its practical advantages, to discuss my gigantic scheme. I was at the end of my money again. Mr. X, however, would not be likely to let me suffer in this respect when I explained the situation. It would be extremely bad policy if nothing else, for him to allow the owner of a patent of such potential value to worry about cash. And for my actual fare and other initial expenses I could rely again on Willy Coulson. *He* would not be the sufferer when I returned to Bramblewick again! His ironic 'Bramblewick' smile had no terror for me now. I felt suddenly exultant in the thought that I had beaten Bramblewick, that never again need I fear that quiet ironic laughter, which itself was like an echo of the laughter of the sea.

The Inspector drew me on one side, and informed me that of course, he could not give me his verdict on the test but that I needn't worry very much as to the contents of the report. Marney had already tied up the claws of the big lobster, and put a looped string on it for carrying. We drew near to the landing posts. The tide had risen over that place on the scaur where, last winter, I had made my remarkable catch of an enamel chamber pot. The Fosdycks' coble was beached. The Fosdycks themselves were standing on the slipway. It was nearly dinner-time. We grounded. The Inspector shook hands with the Lunns and with me, explaining that he had a lunch engagement, and that he must get up to his car as quickly as possible. He wished me good luck in my enterprise, and John, who had jumped out, carried him ashore on his back. John returned, and as soon as the Inspector was out of hearing, he remarked enthusiastically:

'God—he's a nice chap that. One of the nicest I've ever met in my life. Not a bit of swank about him. And yet he's been a naval officer, and I bet he's got any amount of brass. I very nearly asked him whether he'd like to give us a subscription towards the band when we get it going. Did you notice how interested he looked when I mentioned it? Look at the Fosdycks, watching him walk up. They're just waiting to see who it is we've had off with us.'

'He seemed a very nice chap and no mistake,' said Marney. 'He seemed pleased enough, too. I didn't think I'd get those pots up and shot as quick as that. I was all of a tremble inside me when we started for fear summat would go wrong, and he'd laugh at us.'

'They fished well, too,' said John. 'I didn't think they'd fish so well as that straight off, did you, father?'

'I *knew* they would,' Henry answered. 'I *knew* they would. They're better pots than ours all round, miles better, and I don't care who hears me say it. I only wish we had three fleets of them ready for sea now. I shouldn't mind carrying them down through the Dock with all Bramblewick looking on.'

'I wouldn't!' said Marney.

'Nor *I!*' said John; and turning to me. 'How soon do you think you'll be before you start having them made?'

I was still intoxicated, and here was new wine. I told the Lunns that I was going to leave for London to-morrow, and that I must have one of the two bare frames netted to-night. I said that I hoped to be back very soon with as many shut-up pots as they could work from a big motor boat, that would have a mechanical hauling winch, and a cabin. And I was thrilled by the look in their eyes when I told them that the building of this boat would be one of the first things the new Company would do.

I was indeed intoxicated.

EPITAPH

It was a night in late October. A south-east gale was blowing, with heavy squalls of rain. I sat in front of my cottage fire (which Willy Coulson so obligingly had lighted for me) staring into the flames and listening to the sound of the sea on the scaur ends, trying to sum up courage to go round to Marney and tell him I had got back to Bramblewick, and that my patent pot was a failure; that there was to be no fortune for any of us, no new boat, no fleets of shut-up pots, no exciting quests for new lobster grounds, no ideal factory or canneries, no BRITISH IN-SHORE FISHERIES COMPANY, with a trade mark of a symbolic lobster in a lifebelt.

For myself, except that I was worried about money, I was not unduly distressed. Life, it seemed, consisted of the pursuit of phantoms, and was essentially a movement. Happiness was not a static thing but a point in time from which one had a pleasurable perspective ahead or behind. For a year I had found my happiness chiefly in the forward view. My pot, my schemes, had been like an alluring will-o'-the-wisp, leading me on towards an enchanting country, bogging me at times, giving me sly hits, tying the grass under my feet so that I tripped, mocking me, yet for ever giving me such samples of my reward, to keep me pursuing. Now I could look back and see that the pursuit itself had been my reward. There had been little dullness in that year, and many thrills. It had been at least a year of living.

My invention had failed, not because of any intrinsic fault. The official report marked 'available for private circulation only' had been favourable. True it was not enthusiastic; yet it constituted substantial evidence of the practical worth of my pot to the fishermen, and I was given to understand that its cautiously worded approval was far more than the Government usually gave to anything which was to be the subject for commercial exploitation. Unfortunately my arrival in London had almost coincided with Mr. X's departure for one of his prolonged journeys abroad. In an exasperatingly brief interview, he had told me frankly that he would have no time to devote to my invention until his return, the date of which was uncertain. He had given me leave, however, to approach anyone I cared to in search of the capital necessary to secure world patent rights and to begin the manufacture of the pot, on the understanding that any offer I received should be a matter for mutual discussion; and he had obliged me with a cash advance sufficient for me to send Willy a lump off his account, and, provided I was very careful, to keep me going in London for a month.

I had started that search with unbounded optimism: not in any sense discouraged by the fact that had his faith been like mine, Mr. X himself might have provided the requisite sum. London abounded with millionaires and philanthropists, and wealthy business concerns to whom that sum, a minimum of a thousand pounds, would be insignificant. One had only to stand at Hyde Park Corner, and count the number of Rolls-Royces that passed in five minutes to realize it was no fairy tale the streets of London were paved with gold. One had only to look at the palatial blocks of offices, and flats, and shops they were building, and the new Tube stations and picture palaces, and popular cafés, and the six-wheel buses with their soft seats: one had only to watch the shopping crowds in Oxford Street and Regent Street and Kensington; or, in the City, to see the silk-hatted bank messengers hurrying along with black bags full of money to realize that London was a city of stupendous wealth.

It was as though one could hear through all the roar of traffic, the stir and tinkle of a perpetual stream of money, welling out of banks, spilling over the counters of shops, and into the tills of restaurants, and pubs and theatres and picture palaces; into the bags of bus conductors and the pockets of taxi-men, into the automatic tube ticket machines, and cigarette machines, telephones and public lavatories; and flowing back to the banks, where you'd see men in dark clothes, with pale bored faces shovelling heaps of coin with copper shovels, and moving thick wads of pound notes about, with no more concern than if they were packets of cheap stationery. Yet the great electric cables buried under London's roadways are not more adequately insulated from irregular leakage, than the main arteries and veins of this palpable stream of cash.

I lived in cheap lodgings in Brondesbury, over-looking the Queen's Park Station shunting yard. Every morning I set out with my lobster pot in its canvas case, in my search for capital. I had high-placed friends, who although not wealthy themselves, gave me social introduction to persons who were. I was granted interviews with millionaires, with titled philanthrophists of world-wide renown. All of these gentlemen seemed deeply impressed by the pot and by the fact that it had been praised by the Government: all expressed deep sympathy with the British fisherman, and with my scheme for reorganizing the fishing industry: but none offered to take a practical interest in this or the pot itself. I showed the pot to the founder and managing director of one of London's biggest stores: to the director of a famous shipping line, to a director of the Bank of England itself without result. I secured admission to the inner office sanctuary of a famous financier, who a few months later, was languishing in gaol. He had seemed more impressed than any of the other gentlemen I had met, and told me that he thought my pot a very sound proposition, but regretted he was too busy with other things to afford the time for its exploitation. There was, in London at that time, an Anglo-American millionaire who had offered a prize of two thousand pounds for the best suggestion as to how he should dispose of his surplus wealth. The prize unfortunately had already been awarded, but I secured an introduction to him, and explained my schemes. He too, had seemed deeply impressed, and he had asked me to lunch with him at the Savoy Hotel. During that lunch, however, he did nothing but tell me the story of his life (which I had already read in the papers): and he did not mention the pot until we parted: when he told me that he was tired of making money and that it did not interest him from a business point of view. But he wished me very good luck with it.

It was the height of the great speculative boom which

preceded the start of the great world depression. Every day the advertising columns of the press were full of the prospectuses of new companies. The public was invited to invest (and presumably was investing) in concerns for the exploitation of gramophones and gramophone records, of radio apparatus, of colour photography, of cinemas, of patent mattresses, and medicines, of greyhound racing tracks and dirt tracks, of automatic photography machines. Yet I could not persuade anyone to take the responsibility of inviting the public to invest in an invention that was to save men's lives, and save a fine industry from languishing to extinction. It seemed to me that the whole country had gone pleasure mad: that people could think of nothing else but listening to the gramophone or the radio, or going to the pictures, or watching tame dogs chase an electric rabbit, or men falling off motor cycles, or having themselves photographed in six different positions for a shilling in the slot.

I did not despair, however. I would look at every fishmonger's slab I passed on my daily pilgrimage, and often I would stop and inquire the prices of lobsters and crabs: and the smell of raw fish was enough to keep me in mind of the sea and my purpose. The sight of enormous cooked lobsters, draped with parsley and garnished with slices of lemon, in the window of a famous Piccadilly restaurant inspired me with the thought that one day I would see these lobsters bearing the lobster lifebelt trademark. The little bicycle vans that hawk ice-cream in the streets all over London kept me in mind of my plan for a house-to-house delivery of the fresh-caught, fresh-cooked products of BIFCO.

Spring passed and summer came. I had long ago exhausted my advance, and there was still no news of Mr. X's return. I got a small part-time job with an advertising agency, however, which kept me going, and for a fortnight I earned a princely salary looking after a stall at a trade exhibition in Olympia. I did not relax my search, but I changed my tactics. It occurred to me that my invention and its associated schemes had a wider aspect than the purely commercial one. That it was a matter of importance to the State that they should not fail. A Labour Government was in power. I wrote to the Minister of Agriculture and Fisheries himself, explaining how I had failed to obtain the capital necessary to put the manufacture of my patent lobster pot on a practical basis: and suggesting that it might be made the subject for State subsidization, on co-operative socialistic lines. I did not get an encouraging reply. I wrote to the ex-Minister of Agriculture and Fisheries of the Conservative Opposition thinking that he might find some excellent party counter propaganda in the scheme. But I got no reply at all. I remembered that there was a Member of the House of Commons whose whole life had been devoted to the interests of the deep-sea fisherman, and was known as The Fisherman's Friend. I wrote to him and received a letter asking me to have lunch with him at the House, and to bring the pot along. At the public entrance to the House I was accosted by a monumental policeman who asked me what I wanted. I told him that I was lunching with a Member. He asked me what I had got in the bag. I told him it was a lobsterpot. He let me pass with the remark that it was all right so long as it wasn't a camera.

The Fisherman's Friend gave me an excellent lunch. My shut-up pot was demonstrated within the sacred walls of that famous edifice, and within hearing distance of at least two persons whose effigies in white marble or Portland stone would doubtless be preserved for all time within the more sacred portals of an adjacent abbey. But while I thought that one of these persons was giving interested glances at the pot our conversation was not disturbed. The Fisherman's Friend was very interested, and very sympathetic: although he revealed that he had a deep-sea fisherman's mind when he contested my argument that the in-shore fisherman had suffered by illegal trawling. And he saw no hope for me in subsidization, a word of terrifying significance to any member of parliament of any party. What I wanted, in his opinion, was a wealthy man who liked publicity and would not mind paying to have a few thousand pots made and *giving* them to the fishermen, so long as the world would know who had done it.

I did not imagine that Mr.X was quite this sort of man. Throughout that summer however, he remained my one great source of hope. But while he had at last returned to England, it was not until yesterday afternoon that he had been able to give me an interview. In the meantime the great speculative boom had ended in a sensational criminal case, which, as the newspapers said 'rocked the whole structure of British finance to its foundations'. The great depression was setting in.

I did not know whether Mr. X had been involved in

that financial disaster which had ruined so many speculators and investors. There were precious few City men who were not at least indirectly affected by the general depreciation of stocks and shares that it produced. He was kind to me, fatherly almost, but he told me frankly that my chances of securing any sort of financial backing for my pot were nil: and that he himself could not help me further.

It was dark when I left his office near Leadenhall Street. I had my pot with me in its canvas case. I wandered East through the City, paying little attention to where I was going until I found myself in Mark Lane, and I smelt the river. I walked on past the Tower moat, and on to the Tower Bridge, and halted at last in one of those bays, where the pedestrian may stand and look down into the Pool of London. The wind was easterly, and there was a smell in it that was not that of the river only, and of ships, and merchandise and smoke, but of the sea itself. It was raining and cold, with the wind blowing in wild gusts, and I was the only person standing in the bay, so that—waiting for a gap in the stream of vehicular traffic—I could have slipped over without a soul being the wiser. But I had no mind for suicide. The feel of that wet wind in my face, the smell of the distant sea, had roused in me a furious desire to be back in Bramblewick; to be walking on the cliff tops in the wind, or along the scaurs, to be with Marney in the autumn coloured woods, or the kitchen parlour of his cottage, watching his hands in the firelight, listening to the noise of the sea on the cliff below.

And suddenly I knew that I had done with my patent

lobster pot for ever. I saw at last that it, and all my schemes, were phantom. I had enough cash in hand from my 'advertising' job for my fare to Bramblewick, and to pay Willy at least another instalment off his account. He had told me in a letter that I could have the cottage whenever I wished, and that I had only to wire him and he would have the bed aired, a fire lit, and all the groceries I needed taken in.

I would go back to Bramblewick. I did not know what I was going to do when I got there. I had no immediate phantom, save Bramblewick itself. But my conviction that the old one was dead gave me courage to lift my pot in its canvas case over the rails of the Tower Bridge and let it drop into the cold, dark, lobsterless Pool of London.

I changed into my oilskins and sea-boots (which Willy had so obligingly stored for me during my absence), and I could not help thinking of the last time I had worn them and of how optimistic I had been then about the future. I could not help thinking of what I had said to the Lunns, when we had got back from the Government test. I did not relish the task ahead of me. I knew that a big motor coble had been a dream, a phantom, of Henry Lunn ever since he had been obliged to give up the one he had skippered during the war. And I knew that he himself had put great faith in the pot; and that it would be a great disappointment that he was not to be the first fisherman to work a complete equipment of them. But the task had to be done: and I decided that I had best break the news first to Henry Lunn himself.

I quietly opened the door; and I was glad of the wind

and rain, and the darkness and the roar of the sea that would drown the sound of my footsteps. I took a glance at the Brewsters' cottage, and then walked quickly past it to the boundary rail of the Green. Using a torch, I climbed down the slippery path and up the steps to the Lunns' cottage and the warehouse. There was a light in the warehouse. I approached its door timorously, and was about to knock when I remembered that by custom the Lunns never knocked, and regarded it as unfriendly for anyone but a complete stranger to do so.

I opened the door and stepped inside that familiar room and I felt that I had never been away. Henry and Marney were seated on fish boxes in front of the fire, mending lobster pots. They both looked up and smiled genially. I felt the warmth of sincere friendship, but it made me less comfortable in my mind; for, beyond an occasional letter to Marney, in which I had expressed my continued hope of getting my company started, I had told them nothing of what had happened. They were probably thinking, I thought, that my return signified success.

'God,' said Marney, 'it's a queer thing, but we were talking about you, just this very minute. Weren't we father? We knew you were coming back because Willy Coulson said he'd had a wire from you but he didn't say what train, and I was going to come round when I'd finished this pot, and ask you to come and have a bit of supper with us. Find yourself a box, and come and sit by the fire.'

'I'll not shake hands,' said Henry, half-rising, and holding up a tarry paw. 'I'm glad to see you back and no mistake. I was beginning to think we'd never see you again. Sit yourself down. We're just patching up a few old pots in case we get a spell of fine weather, before we start codding. Cod haven't come close in yet, and they won't until we get some snow.'

I sat down. Henry and Marney continued at their task: and there was a prolonged, and to me uncomfortable silence. Then Marney said,

'Well, how did you get on up in London? I got those letters you wrote to me, and I was going to, answer them only there seemed nowt new to say, and I never really got time to sit down quiet and write. How did you get on?'

I had to clear my throat.

'Well,' I said, uncomfortably, 'I'm afraid the whole thing's a failure. It needs a lot of money to get it started, more than I guessed. And I haven't found anyone willing to provide the money. So I've had to give it up.'

I waited, and found courage to look at their faces. But neither showed the slightest sign either of disappointment or resentment.

'No?' said Henry quietly. 'I'm sorry about that.'

'Aye. So am I,' said Marney, calmly cutting an end from a patch of netting. 'I reckoned myself that those folks up in London would be falling over themselves to get hold of it. It's a good idea is that shut-up pot. A damned good idea. Those fifteen you left with us did well, didn't they father?'

'Aye. They fished as well as ours. Better in fact.'

'And they've lasted well, too,' Marney went on. 'We were caught close in with two fleets soon after you'd gone away. We hadn't a chance to go out to them. Most of ours were scrubbed almost to bits when we got to them again. But yours weren't a bit the worse, and they all had lobsters in them.'

'I've often said I wished we had three fleets of them,' said Henry, calmly pursuing his task.

'I was saying the very same thing myself only the other day,' said Marney. 'When we started patching up these old ones. Your pots are twice as easy to mend. You can almost re-net them altogether in the time it takes you to patch up one of ours. . . . Still,' he added philosophically, 'I bet you *would* want a bit of brass to start having them made on a big scale and brass isn't easy to come by these days, although we haven't had a bad year, all things considered.'

'We did well with lobsters,' Henry went on, 'and we'd have done well with salmon if we hadn't lost all our nets the very day before the season ended.'

'We beat the Fosdycks hollow,' said Marney. 'Hollow!'

He laid the pot he had been working on aside, and moved to a pile of pots standing in a corner. He returned with a pot which at first I did not recognize as one of my own. He sat down and put it on his knee.

'Here's one of your pots,' he said. 'You know, I always said that there was one thing wrong with them, and that was they had no side sticks. I knew they wouldn't shut-up if you had them, but working the way we've been doing, along with our pots, it hasn't been worth while bothering to shut them up, and open them again, so when I came to mend the net of this one, thinks I, I'll see what side sticks look like, and I put them on, and put a new net on too, made just the same way as ours instead of it being all joined up like yours: and by doing that I found I could make the doors like ours too. I know it won't shut-up now, but I think you'll agree that it *looks* better. Don't you think so father?'

'It doesn't look that much different from one of ours now,' Henry answered.

'And you can't beat our pots for fishing,' said Marney. Henry grinned.

'There's nowt wrong with our pots except them being so heavy and awkward for stowing, so that you lose them in sudden bad weather. I'd rather have shut-pots any day. But if they can't be got, they can't be got, and that's all there is to say about it. Our pots will do.'

I stared at that pot which had once been a shut-up pot, which now had its cunning catch securely lashed with twine, and its hinged bows made rigid with two stout hazel sticks lashed from end to end: and its net, whose evolution had given me a night of creative agony ending in a morning of elation, replaced with the net whose failure to allow the bows to collapse had caused me nearly to despair. And I glanced at the pot to Henry and Marney Lunn, faithful despite all their protests of being up to date, to their old gear, to their old gods.

And in that moment it seemed that I realized the true splendour of these men whose destinies I had attempted to guide and control. I felt a deep humiliation: and at the same time there stirred in me the first movement of a new creative ecstasy. . . God—if I could only convey some of this splendour in writing; if only I could write a book about the Lunns and the Fosdycks, and their conflict with the sea, without the complications of that 'theme of enmity,' without frills, without any attempt at 'art,' or cleverness: making it *real*, making it *live*, so that it would be a record that in my time such men existed. . .'

A book! A new phantom! I had a sudden fierce desire for pen and paper, to write, and write. . . I got up. Marney had got up too, and was putting on his coat.

'You're coming round to supper aren't you?' he said. 'I told Amy I'd fetch you, if you'd come. We're on with a new rug. It's a blue one this time, with a round thing in the middle, and a fancy border: and this time the prize is two quid. Come on.'

I was too excited to speak coherently or to think whether I should go to Marney's for supper or not: but I mumbled an unsteady good-night to Henry, and, as we moved to the door, and Marney opened it I remembered John, and was about to ask about him when there came from the windy night a blood-curdling howl.

'What the hell's that?' I said.

Marney laughed.

'That?' he echoed. 'That's the Bramblewick Brass Band practising. I was going to tell you in that letter I was going to write that they've got it going, our John and a few other chaps. I'd have been in it too if only I had more time. They had a dance this summer, when all the visitors were here, and they raised enough for their instruments. They've got a local chap to teach them, Harry Thompson, and a damned good hand he is at it too. I think that's LONDONDERRY AIR they're playing now. But they can play HOME SWEET HOME a treat.'

About the author

LEO WALMSLEY was born in Shipley, West Yorkshire, in 1892, and was brought up in Robin Hood's Bay on the North Yorkshire coast — the 'Bramblewick' of several of his novels. After serving with distinction in the Royal Flying Corps in the Great War, where he was awarded the Military Cross, he determined to become a writer, beginning with boys' adventure stories.

He lived for a while in London before returning to Robin Hood's Bay in the late 1920s, then settled in Fowey, Cornwall and wrote *Three Fevers* (1932), the first of his 'Bramblewick' novels, followed by *Phantom Lobster, Foreigners, and Sally Lunn.*

In addition to over twenty books, he wrote 200 or so short stories and articles up to his death in 1966.

For further information about
Leo Walmsley, or membership
of the Walmsley Society,
please visit:

www.walmsleysoc.org

info@walmsleysoc.org